Kenneth E. Wi

HARD DRUGS
a Reality
of Pain!

Published by Kenneth E. Wimbley ISBN: 978-0-578-61082-5

Library of Congress Control Number: 2019918911

I dedicate this project to my beloved parents Jean and Edgar E. Loving, Bill, and Laura Cathcart Wilson.

CONTENTS

I. ACKNOWELDGEMENT

Foremost, I want to acknowledge *God*.

TY to my enthusiastic family members and colleagues, thank you for your encouraging words, and rock-hard support.

Hats off to the warriors out there. Who's been on that train, and who is now schooling the kids, young adults, and adults about the perils of hard drug use?

Hats off to the courageous journalists, anti-drug, health, and faith-based organizations, environmentalists, historians, human rights activists, law enforcement agencies, players, actors, filmmakers, photographers, musicians, poets, and writers for bringing AWARENESS to this vital subject.

II. FOREWORD

Dear valued reader, you have made a WISE investment today.
My name is **Sherman W. Hunter Sr**. Author, Consultant, Podcaster, and Software Developer.

I met Ken in 1986, during a time when I and my partner, **Harvey Brody**, a well-known engineer, successful inventor, and prolific marketing mastermind, were publishing and marketing business courses and newsletters for aspiring entrepreneurs.

From our earliest conversations, I recall Kenneth displayed a keen appreciation of the importance of personal character, truth, and "maintaining a positive self-worth."

His latest PROJECT! "**Hard Drugs, a Reality *of* Pain!**"
He expressed would function as a LIFELINE and EDUCATIONAL vehicle for the masses.

Ladies and gentlemen, his stroke of genius has produced a masterpiece, one you can appreciate having around in the 21st century.
· Alcohol and drug use are transforming many lives for the worse.
· Today, you're going to be enlightened by a warrior whose experience takes Drug Awareness and Drug Prevention Education to a new level of awesomeness.
· Over the past twenty-plus years, we have lost great minds, and amazing talent to hard drugs.

The ever-present THREATS of drugs and alcohol use is rising among teens, young adults, and adults.
Reading Ken's manuscript, its power struck me.
He delivers a thought-provoking opening, introduction, and theme you'll find engaging.
This is not a book to GLANCE over, it is far-reaching.
How he communicates his timely thoughts and findings with you is exceptional.
I'm honored to have written this FOREWORD.

I'll leave you with some instructions.

Relax and read, listening to your favorite music, or to no music.

Let history and the spoken word take you there!

Your desire for Drug Awareness and Drug Prevention Education.

For something different, ultramodern.

Experience "Hard Drugs, a Reality *of* Pain!"

With your family, friends, and with the questioner who needs to be enlightened by it.

Sherman W Hunter, Sr.
Director - SDK Hunter Consultant Group
(SDK Hunter LLC)

· Please see
Chapter 48. Opportunities In Real Time.

III. OPENING

Genesis 1

Verse 11:
And *God* said,
let the earth burst
forth with every sort
of grass and seed-

bearing plants.
And let there be
trees that grow
seed bearing fruit.

The seeds will then
produce the kinds of
plants and trees from
which they came.
And so, it was.

Verse 12:
The land was filled
with seed bearing
plants and trees
of like kind.

And *God* saw
that it was good.

Genesis 2:17

But from the tree
of *good* and *evil*
you shall not eat
of it, for in the
day you eat
from it.

You shall
surely die.

IV. INTRODUCTION

"**Good,** superior to the average.
Satisfactory, beneficial to health,
having the qualities that are desirable
or distinguishing in a particular thing."

"**Evil,** distorts peace, and happiness.
It destroys the perfection
of one's natural being."

—Webster's Dictionary

Going back to the medieval age. 3400 B.C. and the Huaca Prieta settlement in Peru, 2500-1800 B.C. History tells us that the **cannabis, coca,** and **opium** plants have played an important role in our existence.

For **900+ years**, the "exploitation" of the **coca** and **opium** plants has brought chaos into the lives of millions from all levels of society.

In 1906, Cannabis, **Hemp** took on a lot of propaganda.

1906-to-1937, thirty-one years of yellow journalism. The great queen, *Cannabis,* lost her standing to cotton, fossil fuels, synthetic meds, and timber.

The natural order
of things is
in broken
pieces.

O*pium!*
"From the tree
of good and
evil, you
shall not
eat of it, for
in the day
you eat from
it, **YOU** shall
surely die."

On Earth,
God created
a paradise.

In it, He
sowed the
seeds of
good and
evil.

One alluring,
yet deceiving
FLOWER, that
evolves into
a green fruit,
the likes of a
green apple
with its Crown,
Capsule, and
Pod visible,
stood out
above all
the other
plants in
the garden.

In the heart
of this fruit,
there is good
and evil!

It's **evil** is the
likes of which
HUMANKIND
wishes they
had never
known.

Opium is a member of the *Papaveraceous* family.
Opium Papaver Somniferum L. elite.

It is the most popular of its kind, grown in **Anatolia,** the *Garden of Eden.* Its likeness is that of a green fruit, deceiving.
One of the longest wars in history was between The Ottoman Empire and The Byzantine Eastern Roman Empire, 1299-to-1453, 154 years of warring.
The Ottomans owned and controlled the opium fields of **Anatolia,** their ground forces carried opium into battle with 'em. They ate and drank it for courage, pressing ahead, winning battle after battle.
This news reached the ears of the Roman Catholic Church, who declared.
"That anything from the east was taboo, a link to the *Devil.*" **Whose whisper can be very persuasive.**
The Ottomans elite forces, their perseverance and super cannons brought down the walls of the Eastern Roman Empire.
On May 29, 1453. The 21-year-old Sultan Mehmed II proclaimed **Constantinople,** present day **Istanbul** as the future Ottoman Empire.

· Please see
https://www.youtube.com/watch?v=VIQaepoKqYg
https://en.wikipedia.org/wiki/Fall_of_Constantinople
https://en.wikipedia.org/wiki/Mehmed_the_Conqueror and

The Ottomans possessed one of earth's most **priceless** gems! *Opium Papaver Somniferum L. elite*. The cream of opium.
The Ottoman's arms reached far and wide with this **seed-bearing fruit.**
Popular for its purity. The demand for its aphrodisiac and medicinal properties was over the top.
The citizens of Ottoman enjoyed blending opium, poppy seeds, spices, and herbs in their meals. They had a desire for their own opium/product.
The demand for *Opium Papaver Somniferum L. elite* from within the Empire exceeded their exports to China, Europe, France, the Netherlands, Portugal, and Spain.
These buyers sailed around the Ottomans' BRAND, taking big bites out of the *Golden Apple.*

The Ottomans Empire prospered from the sales of opium, furs, silk, from halal, and haram businesses.
• Please see
The Ottoman Empire - Wikipedia

During the 1500s. The Portuguese and the Dutch East, their merchants, and crew, took pleasure in smoking opium with a blend of tobacco. A **recipe** the Portuguese and the Dutch introduced to their Southeast Asia customers who, like them, had no farseeing eyes (or) foresight to see, that, from this pleasure.
A GREATER EVIL was in the making.
There were TRILLIONS to be had.
The Devil's endgame! Destroy, kill, and rob. The WEALTH gain from trafficking in opium got the **Portuguese East India Company's** attention.
So-much-so, they designed a plan to control traffic in the Indian Ocean. On August 24, 1511. Portugal's military launched a bloody assault on Malacca.
The launching pad to India's opium fields and all of Asia.
• Please see
http://en.wikipedia.org/wiki/Capture_of_Malacca_(1511)

130 years later, 1641, the **Dutch East India Company**, and the **East India Company** joined forces and seized Portugal's glory, and with it the world's busiest seaport.
• Please see
http://en.wikipedia.org/wiki/Dutch_Malacca.

This was a COSMIC score for the British East and Dutch East India Companies.
Still in the drug game, the Portuguese East India Company maintained opium factories in China, where smoking opium with tobacco went on for days, months, years.
At the turn of the **17th** century, **Madak** was on the scene.
A **new** recipe for smoking opium, a blend of medicinal hemp, herbs, and less tobacco; a practice that reached epidemic proportions.
In the year 1720, **The Qing Dynasty** saw Madak smoking as a "social evil for the well to do, and poor."
• Please see
https://en.wikipedia.org/wiki/Madak

Protecting the welfare of his community, the Yongzheng Emperor enacted the first **Anti-Opium Decree**, in 1729, prohibiting Madak, and the buying and selling of opium.

In secrecy, his enemies stored up crates of opium, medicinal hemp, herbs, and tobacco in local warehouses.

The Dutch East was in CONTROL at that point.

Their competitors, The Company, The East India Company, The Honourable East India Company, and The East India Trading Company.

These British owned firms was the Dutch East India Company and China's worse nightmare coming.

Behind the scenes, Britain's business relationship with India dates to the 1600s. **India** was their means to achieving their economic and imperialist goals.

Over 40 years' time, the British built up its military forces and a fleet of ships. This significant accomplishment set the stage for their biggest campaign ever.

The Company placed into orbit, **The English, British Corporation**. Set up to trade in the Indies and Southeast Asia countries.

· Please see

https://en.wikipedia.org/wiki/Presidencies_and_provinces_of_British_India and https://en.wikipedia.org/wiki/East_India_Company https://en.wikipedia.org/wiki/Joint-stock_company

In 1647, **"The Company"** had twenty-three factories and ninety employees working in India.

Sixty years later, 1707, they renamed The Company, **The British East India Company**. The **Rhino** in the room. The Board of Directors, their vision of company rule in **India**; materialized.

From the 1600s to 1756, **156 years**, Britain's business relationship with **India** presented themselves as of wealth and power. However, there was one last victory to achieve. 1757, the Battle of Plassey.

For their successes; they received the keys to **India's** prime real estate, to her cities, her raw materials, hemp farms, tobacco, and opium fields, to the Indian subcontinent, and the Indian ocean, the world's third largest.

· Please see

https://en.wikipedia.org/wiki/Indian_Ocean

They collected taxes and fees and got a sweet deal in contracts and concessions covering North America, North Africa, Persia, and the Southeast Asia markets.

This was the biggest merger in the history of imperialism.

13 years into their success, they endured two crop failures, one in the fall of 1768, and another in the summer of 1769.

The British East India Company blew it big time when they cultivated **opium** and **indigo** plants over **food** crops.

The Bad News!

· Please see

http://en.wikipedia.org/wiki/Bengal_famine_of_1770

While this unfortunate situation was unfolding in India.

The demand for opium back in China soared upwards to the Devil's throne.

Revisiting the year 1729, under the leadership of The Yongzheng Emperor, China's annual opium imports from the Dutch East India Company were at two hundred chests.

· Please see

https://upload.wikimedia.org/wikipedia/commons/1/1f/Opium_
Chests_%2810097967923%29.jpg

Thirty-plus years later, during the 1750s, opium production in the **Golden Triangle** added tons more of opium to China's unwanted inventory from the British.

Forty-nine years later, 1799, the demand for opium throughout Southeast Asia spiral out of control, millions of Chinese citizens were addicted to opium. The drug cartels creeped in. The **Anti-Opium laws** lost their footing. In the year, 1800, China's annual opium imports increased to 4,500 chests.

The British East India Company maintained warehouses in India. Stocked with opium to be shipped to China, and to North America's opium merchants, and to merchants around the world.

Who played a key role in market expansions, and in developing additional players and sources of buyers.

By 1838, China was warehousing 40,000 chests. Business between **BEIC** and **China** wasn't on an equal playing field.

The British tried balancing their shortfalls by twisting China's arm. China unleashed the dragon.

The following year 1839, the **Emir** seized and destroyed 1400 tons of opium being warehoused in secrecy. The British double-dealings triggered the **first** opium war.

From 1839 to 1842. Eighteen years later, the dispute over **BEIC'S** deception deepen launching a **second** opium war waged by Britian and France, from 1856 to 1860.

• Please see

https://en.wikipedia.org/wiki/Opium_Wars and (1) opium wars - YouTube

China lost the second opium war, opium imports reached 70,000 chests, 4,480 tons.

"This number corresponds with the global production of opium in the new millennium, the year **2000**."

• Please see

https://en.wikipedia.org/wiki/History_of_opium_in_China
And The Aftermath of The British East India Company.
https://en.wikipedia.org/wiki/East_India_Company#References

The Golden Apple!
"The day you eat from it
you shall surely die."

By the 1900s, the world community was wrestling with a massive opiate problem. In 1905, the United States Congress banned opium.

A year later, 1906, The American Medical Association gave Bayer AG the green light to distribute their brand, **HEROIN**.

A crippling decision, from 1906-to-1907, within one year, twenty-five million people worldwide were addicted.

"1.5% of the world population, source UNODC, 100 years of drug control."

In 1908, President Theodore Roosevelt's administration convened in Shanghai to meet with the world leaders to discuss a serious matter they were all experiencing, an opioid epidemic.

The *Devil's* plan to weaponize opium to do his evil bidding against humankind was succeeding.

On February 9, 1909, the U.S. Opium Exclusion Act went into effect. Five years later, Francis Burton Harrison, Governor-General of the Philippines signed the Narcotics Act on December 17, 1914. This law was passed with no intentions of "enforcing" prohibition.

"The (IRS) Internal Revenue Services imposed a special tax upon all persons who produced, imported, manufactured, dealt in, distributed, or gave away **poppy** or **coca leaves**, their salts, and byproducts for nonmedical purposes."

The Harrison Narcotics Tax Act. Promoted the "orderly" marketing of **opium, cocaine, heroin,** and other drugs for retail sales, and for sale on a physician's prescription-only basis.

It was confirmed "that MDs were allowed to prescribe **opium, cocaine,** and **heroin,** for normal treatment, but not for addiction."

Those physicians found guilty of doing otherwise paid a fine or went to jail.

• Please see

https://www.naabt.org/documents/Harrison_Narcotics_Tax_Act_1914.pdf

These bittersweet laws opened *Pandora's* Box.

By the 1920s, drug trafficking, and the number of drug users increased by the millions.

Bootleg booze, designer drugs; cannabis, cocaine, heroin, opium, and tobacco smoking were part of the social norm.

Bootleggers, dealers, hustlers, musicians, party goers, gangsters, pimps, street walkers, and Johns lined up to get on board the hell train.

The Black Market was BOOMING!

In the 1930s, whisky and opium dens were popping up in the big cities. In the 1940s, 50s, 60s, 70s, the opium trade continued to make **VAST** sums of money through the French and Cuba Connections.

• Please see

https://en.wikipedia.org/wiki/French_Connection and
https://en.wikipedia.org/wiki/Havana_Conference#Narcoticstrade

For one-thousand two hundred plus years, to date.

The nefarious forces behind synthetic opium is INCREASING the odds of addiction.

· **Please see**
Special_Points_WDR2023_web_DP.pdf (unodc.org)
full documentary Opium, Morphine & Heroin - YouTube
(264) synthetic opioids - YouTube
(43) fentanyl - YouTube

CANNABIS, HEMP,
ARE THE SAME PLANT

Cannabis Sativa L. Sativa means cultivated,
and the **L.** Comes from the name **Carolus Linnaeus**
who defined the plant.
· **Please see**
https://en.wikipedia.org/wiki/Carl_Linnaeus

Cannabis, Hemp, is the most **phenomenal** plant on the planet. "It is the **first known** plant species to be the most resourceful for human needs."
The demand for Hemp in North America was so hot that in 1619. **The First Marijuana Law** in Jamestown Colony, VA. was legislated.
Farmers in that region were **ordered** to grow **hemp** or go to jail. This measure was enforced in Massachusetts in 1631, Connecticut in 1632, and in the Chesapeake territories in the 1700s.
For 200 + years, **this law was mandatory.**
The demand for cannabis, hemp was enormous.

It was so high, the government used **hemp paper** to print **Bank Notes,** from 1631 to the 1800s.
· Please see
(17) Hemp is RIGHT ON THE MONEY! - YouTube

This plan was a motivational tool to encourage farmers to grow more hemp.
In 1849, the call to action, to plant, harvest, and process hemp increased the demand for manual labor in the state of Kentucky.
In 1906, bureaucrats dragged *Cannabis* through the mud.
In the year 1923, seventeen years of fake news destroyed *Cannabis'* GREAT reputation. With the aid of oil barons, politicians, pulpwood billionaires, and overzealous investors and the Marijuana Tax Act of 1937 buried her.
The Pure Food and Drug Act labeled the *Queen* Cannabis a poison. In 1961, the Single Convention on Narcotics Drugs discontinued her **multiple** uses.
For completeness, this **International Treaty** labeled *Cannabis*
a **Schedule II drug**. For years, this rhetoric appealed to our emotions rather than to our rational way of thinking.
On December the 13th, and 20th, 2018. The-powers-that-be in Washington, DC. Signed the **Hemp Farm Bill** into law.
Giving *Cannabis* a LEGAL playing field.
Cannabis News, April 1, 2022. The House passed legislation to Decriminalize Marijuana at the federal level.
October 6, 2022. President **Joe Biden,** voiced **pardons** for individuals imprisoned for a simple marijuana possession.
He also publicized **rescheduling** *Cannabis* from a **Scheduled II drug.** An extraordinary move against **deforestation,** and **fossil fuel** dependance.
North America's founding fathers were advocates for a thriving Cannabis, Hemp industry. President George Washington farmed hemp. Thomas Jefferson imported hemp seeds.
In 1750, Benjamin Franklin opened the first Hemp Paper Mill. **133 years later,** 1883, 75% to 90% of all paper globally was made from hemp.
· Please see
https://en.wikipedia.org/wiki/Hemp_paper

One of the world's leading entrepreneurs and automaker.
Mr. Henry Ford, joined forces with two of the world's most celebrated biologist and inventors? Mr. George Washington Carver and Mr. Thomas Alva Edison.

According to legitimate sources, Mr. Ford, Mr. Washington, and Mr. Edison were all in on producing *hemp* and other crops for industrial uses.
"They saw no need to exploit the earth for her fossil fuels, and trees."
· Please see
https://ushempmuseum.us/chemurgy

In 1937, Mr. Ford's Chemist, Mr. Robert Allen Boyer, invented a "curved plastic sheet" made from the properties of soybean.
This plastic was so promising it would not bend or shatter.
"He hoped his invention would replace **steel** in the auto body industry."
· Please see
https://en.wikipedia.org/wiki/Robert_Boyer_(chemist)
Meet the Engineer behind Mr. Ford's plastic car, Mr. Lowell E. Overly.
· Please see
(396) Lowell E. Overly designer of fords plastic car - YouTube
and
https://en.wikipedia.org/wiki/Soybean_car

In addition to these major accomplishments, Mr. Ford, Mr. Carver, and Mr. Edison developed a **cleaner FUEL** using hemp and natural crops.
While we're on the subject about fuel. **Mr. Rudolf Diesel**, the inventor of the diesel engine, designed his engines to run on **hemp**, and **peanut oil**, one of Mr. Carver's discoveries.
These entrepreneurial giants were pioneers. Looking out for mother earth, and for every breathing, living being and thing on it.

Cannabis is the most **sought-after** recreational and **medicinal** plant-based drug on the planet, with proof of a lengthy history dating back to 2737 BCE, China.
· Please see
https://en.wikipedia.org/wiki/Cannabis
http://en.wikipedia.org/wiki/History_of_medical_cannabis

Now, with a revolution BUDDING in the 21st century.
· Please see
www.youtube.com/results?search_query=industrial+hemp+

Cannabis has all the NATURAL it takes to compete with synthetic meds, and billions of trees that are being cut down daily.

Eighty percent of these trees are cut down for paper products. "Another process that pollutes the air."

Growing hemp is the immediate SOLUTION to deforestation.

· Please see

(397) deforestation documentary - YouTube and

(396) global warming disasters - YouTube

Imagine the damage you just seen being reversed with the aid of this plant, *Cannabis, Hemp* bringing forth healthy, safe, and sound developments. **Imagine** the Artic, Greenland ice sheet, and the Himalayas refreezing!? Looking up, seeing blue skies in the big cities where smog dominates the atmosphere. **Imagine** pleasant temperatures, no more extreme weather events, hot summers, fires, floods, breathing problems.

Are you a SKEPTIC?

· Please see

Home – Climate Change: Vital Signs of the Planet (nasa.gov)

and NRDC https://www.nrdc.org/about

Let's talk about the *COCA* plant. The abuse of its **Alkaloids** puts one's future in the hands of APOLLYON.

It's positive **BENIFITS** outweigh its dark side.

Please read **The Divine Plant of the Incas.** By John Uri Lloyd and John Thomas Lloyd, 1911.
· Please see
www.swsbm.com/ManualsOther/Coca.pdf
https://en.wikipedia.org/wiki/Coca

The coca leaves are rich in nutrients.
From a **(food)** perspective.
Please see The Nutritional Value of Coca. And the Internet Archive. By James A. Duck, David Aulik, and Timothy Plowman, **Botanical Museum Leaflets, Harvard University**, October 31, 1975.
· Choose a download, (*pdf file*).
https://archive.org/details/cbarchive_133680_nutritionalvalueofcocaleaf9999

Also See Chapters 49 and 50. In the light of what's been shared here today. It is imperative that you have some knowledge about **Clandestine Chemistry.**
· Please see
https://en.wikipedia.org/wiki/Clandestine_chemistry

The question we should ALL be asking ourselves is, where do these toxic liquids and chemicals **wind up** after they're disposed of!?!
The answer, they're moving **undetected** through our water system. Read and weep.
· Please see
https://pubmed.ncbi.nlm.nih.gov/28843086

The natural order of things is in broken pieces.
The Creator Created a Horn of Plenty!

We hold high Mother Earth's
stunning beauty, her design,
her power and wealth.

We BENIFIT from her
richness, her secrets.
And we create from
them living hells,
personal heavens.

Exploiting her!
GREED has spoiled
the hoarder.

Time roots out
and removes
predatoriness.

Heaven's patience
with GREED is
wearing thin.

The Court of Conscious is Real.

OPEN MIC

PROSE N POETRY

CHAPTER I

TRAIN RIDE TO HELL!

Believers and
Nonbelievers.

First timers,
losers, winners,
the good, bad,
mean, bold,
young, and
old are on
this train
ride to hell.

We're drinking,
drugging,
hustling,
and sin
goes on
for days
on end.

365 day's
this train to
hell is
blazing down
hell's tracks!
Fiery hot.
Sizzling in
degradation,
and guilt.

That's local,
and global

gossip.

World News.

Those souls
boarding will
find nothing
but addiction,
deceit, death and
self-destruction
there!

No one cares,
nor are they
cared for
on that
train ride
to Hell.

OPEN MIC

PROSE N POETRY

CHAPTER 2

WHO I'M I?
I'M KING HEROIN

An experiment
of morphine,
the offspring
of opium.

In the streets!
I'm alias
murder one,
aka black tar,
the boy, smack,
aka China white,
the white horse,
aka fentanyl.

I'm that feeling
of eloquence,
I'm that
fire running
through
every junkie's
vein.

CURIOUS?

Once you
learn the
rules of
engagement.

How to snort,
skin pop, and
mainline my
passion.

You won't
be curious
anymore,
you won't
be alone,
come along.

I do teens,
men and
women,
I do the
blind and
the crippled.

It's not
about your
socioeconomic
status either.

You can count
on me to
deliver.

You can bet
on your life,
on your soul,
my addiction
is unlike
any other.

I'm so good,
that, first-
timers will
come back
for another
fix, they'll
risk their soul
for Heroin.

I'm so loved
that for all
the WRONG
reasons, they
love me even
more!

Yes, apart
from their
dying veins,
on that train
ride to hell.

Soon! They'll
be spiking
their toes,
their genitals.

Who am I?
I'm King Heroin!

The 800-pound
gorilla, who's
looking to
ride your
back, for
years to come.

OPEN MIC

PROSE N POETRY

CHAPTER 3

DIACETYLMORPHINE

The birth of Heroin.

In the year
1804, Friedrich
W.A. Serturner
isolated *Morphine*
from opium.

He named his
lucky strike
Morphium,
after the
Greek god
of dreams,
Morpheus.

70 years later,
the year 1874,
Mr. C.R. Alder
Wright, a master
chemist, physics
researcher, and
founder of the
Royal Institute
of Chemistry,
was the first
to synthesize
Diacetylmorphine,
HEROIN.

Mr. Wright

recorded *heroin*
to be 2-to-3
times more
powerful
than *morphine*,
and UNSAFE
to administer.

After his passing
in 1894, four
years later,
his notes
turned up in
the **Chemical &
Pharmaceutical
Journal**.

Reading it,
Mr. Heinrich
Dreser came
across Mr.

Wrights
fallen angel.

Working for
Bayer AG as a
chemist, and
the inventor
of **codeine.**

Heinrich passed
his findings
on to Felix
Hoffmann,
the inventor
of **aspirin**, and
the resurrector of
Diacetylmorphine.

Bayer was sure
of themselves
that **Heroin**
was a cure
for asthma,
coughs, pain,
pneumonia, and
for sleepless
nights.

After four
years of
TESTING.

In the year
1898, Bayer
marketed
Heroin as
a brand.

Using global
advertising
and a lot of
publicity!

Heroin was
a household
name in 23
nations.

In 1906, the
American
Medical
Association
approved
Heroin for
public use.

In 1924, the
wonder drug
turned out to
be a homicidal
demon selling
on the black
market as a
leisure drug
to snowbirds,
junkies. Tying
off the dragon.

And functional
addicts, working
40 hrs. And OT
for a fix, for a
snort, for a
ride on that
white horse?

GIDDY-UP!

365 days,
Heroin is
their quest
for new and
exotic sensations.

That only through
a reawakening,
determination,
and sadly,
death can
they part
from it.

Diacetylmorphine,
heroin, the
offspring of
morphine,
the offspring
of Opium.

"For in the day
you eat from it.
YOU shall surely die."

The Rest Is History!

(49) heroin addiction globally - YouTube

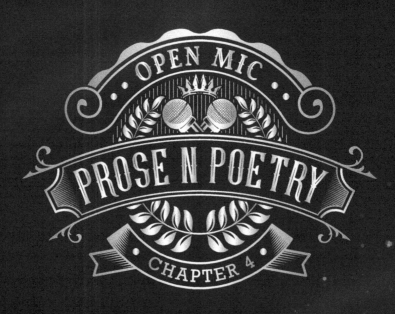

OPEN MIC

PROSE N POETRY

CHAPTER 4

CLANDESTINE CHEMISTRY

The Chemical
Gold Rush!
Drug making
in secrecy.

ILLEGLY,
there could
be a rocket
scientist in your
neighborhood
cooking up
synthetic
drugs.

The likes of
crack, meth,
and fentanyl,
MIXING it up
with cocaine,
and Wildnil, the
SERIAL KILLERS.

OPEN MIC

PROSE N POETRY

CHAPTER 5

THE MOST WANTED
& UNWANTED

The most wanted
and unwanted
hard drugs
out there!

You can't ignore
the history about
drug dealing
and drug
trafficking.

Surviving for
900 + years
is real for
another
100 years.

The GAME
survives on
money, and
from the lack
of it!

For another
100 years
you'll hear
about 'em,
being in the
most never
thought of
places, were
you'll find
the GREEDY,

worshiping
their drugs
as deities, gods.

The most wanted
and unwanted
ones in pursuit
of you, the
curious and
the naïve who
has yet to see,
feel, and encounter
their evil.

OPEN MIC

PROSE N POETRY

CHAPTER 6

FIRST TIME MOM
ADDICTED

The charming
young lady
standing in
front of the
mirror, she
doesn't know
yet, she's six
weeks into
her pregnancy.

The problem is,
she spends
her evenings
after work
sipping on
red wine
till bedtime.

On the week-
ends, she parties,
with her friends,
with the rum
and cocaine.

Coming down
off the Caine,
she pops an
opioid pill.

The problem
with her being
pregnant is
she's two
years into
drinking
and drugging.

The news of
her having
a baby girl
doesn't move
her! She's into
her feelings of
excitement.

Into denial
about her
baby girl,
coming into
this world a
junkie, jonesing.

She's not
imagining
at all what
that alcohol,
cocaine, and
opioid is about
to put her and
her daughter
through!

If she could
only imagine
her FEARS!
Hearing her
screams!

If she could
only imagine
her PAIN!
Imagine
looking into
her swollen
eyes, cause of
her nonstop
crying.

If she could
only imagine

feeling her
seizures, the
tubes running
down her nose
and throat, her
fight to breathe,
to persevere.

First time mom
addicted,
imagine you
suffering with
her anxieties?!

Gasping for
your breath!
Imagine the
STRESS!

Imagine having
a life shattering
reason to not
be drinking,
and drugging
during your
pregnancy!

Imagine you,
coming into
this world,
cold turkey,
jonesing.

Imagine the
TRAUMA!
Imagine
your little
girl cuddle
up in your
arms going
home after
enduring a
living hell.

Imagine looking
upon her delicate
body, into her
eyes, it breaks
your heart
to see her
BROKEN.

It's hard for
you to come
to grips with
this reality!

It hurts!

First Time Mom
Addicted!

IMAGINE
STOPPING
the drinking,
and drugging,
while he, she,
sleeps quietly
in your midst.

IMAGINE it!

OPEN MIC

PROSE N POETRY

CHAPTER 7

LISTEN!

Hard drugs
is the *Devils*
game plan
for ensnaring
the righteous
and unrighteous
folks.

His sleight
of hand is
deceiving
millions.

And millions
are buying
into his
guarantees.

Selling off
their SOULS
for a living
hell without
end.

OPEN MIC

PROSE N POETRY

CHAPTER 8

BEHIND
THE SCENES I

Fiction and
nonfiction
make for good
storytelling
about drug
addiction,
drug dealing,
and life behind
bars.

Fiction and
nonfiction fused
make surprising
jaw-dropping
drama with the
fake drugs,
fake crimes,
with the fake
violence, and
gun scenes
unfolding.

RAT-TAT-TAT!
BANG! BANG!
Fiction in living
color. Rated
B. R. PG.

NONFICTION
action! The *Devil*
is real! Hell on
earth is real!

Young people
are OD'ing!
Killing! And
don't know
why is real!

Someone's going
to jail every ninety
seconds for a
drug violation
is real, with
the actual
players, and
swingers, with
the shadowy
figures in the
dark.

FICTION is a
work of ART!

NONFICTION
is based on
the REAL!

**SMILING FACES!
INVISABLE MADNESS!**

Behind-the-Scenes II.

OPEN MIC

PROSE N POETRY

CHAPTER 9

BEHIND THE SCENES II

It's Diablos!

Entertaining
his GLOBAL
audience
with his
nefarious
plan for
the living.

That's played
out in life, in
books, in prose,
and poetry, in
music, and
movies, were
nonfiction
and fiction
get intense.

**Rated R,
PG, X.**

Booze, Crimes,
Drugs, Sex,
and Violence.

Behind The Scenes II.

Mirroring the
lifestyle of
millions who
have accepted
Diablos' invitation!

To live their life
as a functional
addict, a dealer,
a fille de joie'
a corrupt cop,
individual,
judge, politician,
villains.

The CAST in
his dramatic
piece.

Who believe
Diablo saying,
it's too late
to change*!*

Too late to
get CLEAN*!*

Too late to
get out of
the game.

Too late to
undo his
promise, to
deceive you
with his evil
counsel.

Listen*!*
Below the
threshold of
your conscious,
you hear *Diablo*
whispering,
planting bad
thoughts in
your head:

You fall
for his plot*!*

**Behind the
Scenes II.**

You'll find
yourself
playing a
devilish role*!*

Rated R. PG.

OPEN MIC

PROSE N POETRY

CHAPTER 10

GAMES

The highway
robbers in this
game is the
booze and
the controlling
substance.

You open up
your world
to BOTH!
You open
Pandora's
Box!

To evils
invisible, to
the vicious side
of addiction,
to the portal
of HADIS,
it's in
the cards.

The players are
UNSURE of
what they
believe in!

In *God*, in
money, or
in that drink
and drug
they trust,
that's playing
'em.

PLAYERS!
There's no
number one
trophy holders,
gold, bronze,
silver medalists
in this game.

The GAME

takes no
prisoners.

The losers
got a lot of
free time,
prison time
to reminisce.

To fantasize
about
how much
m o n e y
they had!

About the
good and
the bad
times they
had!

OPEN MIC

PROSE N POETRY

CHAPTER 11

POPPING PILLS

Are you into
pills, club
drugs,
synthetic
opioids!?

The likes of
CARFENTANIL
"that's **10,000**
times more
potent than
morphine
and **100** times
more potent than
FENTANYL."

Both will
KILL you
faster than
a party pill
will!

They're projectiles.
AIMING for
the heart.

You know
about the pill
CAPTAGON!?

Its chemical name
is Fenethylline,
it's sold on the
streets as an
amphetamine.

"Designed to
give you a
FALSE
sense of
courage."

CURIOUS?
Drop One!
You may or
may not live
to decide,
if that pill
is for you
or not.

Just Know!
FENTANYL
mixed with
CARFENTANIL,
is a deadly
mix, a deadly
game of Russian
Roulette.

POPPING PILLS!
It won't be in
your favor
when that
little pill
cause you
to lose your
most prized
possession!

Your Soul,
you pray
the Lord
will save.

CURIOUS?

LISTEN to
the millions
of hearts
beating
hard, out
of control.

Out of
panic of
an overdose!

POPPING PILLS!

OPEN MIC

PROSE N POETRY

CHAPTER 12

!!WARNING!!

My name is
Crack! Crack
Cocaine,
CC for short.

I travel the
seven seas
with ease.
I'm bought
with cash,
sex, and
valuables only.

Your first hit!
Everything
you own,
including
your soul
belongs to
me.

Your name
and fame
will be out
of sight,
out of mind.

Feeling no
pain! I'll
maintain
on robbing
you blind.

And to
add to your
misfortunes,
I'm gonna
hurt you
real, bad.

Make you
wish, you
wasn't born,
best you
remember
that, and
know this!

My Aliases;
some folks
call me love,
old school
caviar,
Hard rock,
coke for
short.

Best believe,
I'm a *Devil* to
support. I'll kill
your appetite,
blow your
mind, and
welcome
you to hell
at the same
time!

Believe!
I've hooked
the bold, the
strong, and
the weak
minded.

And have
led them one
by one to a
troublesome
and painful
life they wish
they had never
known.

My true value?
I'm more
valuable
than Gold.

Before the
METH
epidemic,
I was out
of control.

Today, we're
companions
rolling with
the worst,
of 'em.

Since the 1980s,
millions have
fallen victim
to my poison,
to my criminal
activities, my
injustice.

Because of
my reputation
as a control
substance,
their numbers
are rising!

Smokers, and
dealers addicted
to my game,
shouldn't
hold me to
blame for
your failures!

It's your love
for me and
what I can do
for you is
what's driving
you insane.

Since my
transformation
from powder
cocaine to
crack cocaine,
teens, young
adults, and
adults have
fallen beneath
my white
wings.

I'm the big
white bird,
with droppings
of green!

Who I'm I!?
I'm Crack
Cocaine!
CC for short!

You can
best believe,
I'll steal your
hopes and
dreams.

You see! I'm
the goddess
of misery,
the princes
of crime.

You start
liking me.
You're going
to die, or do
some time.

You might
get lucky,
and go into
a Rehab, but
that's no sure
thing!

I'll change
your mind
with a blast
from a glass
pipe!

I'll have you
feigning,
stealing.
I'll get you
killed. Make
you kill, take
your life
by suicide.

O' you don't
believe!?
You think
I'm a tease?

Please, look
back on my
HISTORY!
In the 1980s,
90s, to this
very day! I've
put millions
in hospitals,
in prison, in
their graves.

I've put millions
in the streets,
I'm just that
deep!

You see!
It doesn't
matter, not
to me, who
you love,
are, were
you sleep.

You won't be
free of me,
you'll be
smoking
Crack in
your dreams.

You get clean
and relapse!
Back to the
life of
Dr. Jekyll
and Mr. Hyde.

I've turned a
lot of good,
and evil
people into
baseheads,
thugs, thieves,
and Wannabe
drug dealers,
and gangsters.

SMOKERS and
dealers it's on
you to want
to live are
die, go to
hell, or do
some time.

For the MONEY!

I'll be around!
Till you or
your kids
come by.

WHO am I?
Crack Cocaine.
CC for Short!

OPEN MIC

PROSE N POETRY

CHAPTER 13

FROM HELL'S DEEP!

The *Devils*
Aphrodisiac!
Crack Cocaine.
Demon among
Demons.

When you
inhale, exhale,
the *Devil's*
white smoke,
a sense of
forbidden
SEX pervades
the immediate
atmosphere.

15 minutes
later, your
feening for
that feeling,
for another hit!

After inhaling
and exhaling,
the *Devil*,
appeals to
the FLESH,
15 minutes
later, he
whispers
take another
hit!

Wired! Chasing
that feeling.
Down to
Kibbles n bits,
the last hit.

Strung Out!
Weak for it!

No hard cash
on hand, time
to roll to the
bank. No
money to
burn. Ask
the dealer
for credit,

with interest,
you got it!

Two days
gone by,
can't sleep,
loss of
appetite.

The Central
Nervous
System
is a mess.

Regretting
the moment.
Too late, the
cravings are
hell's deep!

The mind
and body
is a slave to
Crack Cocaine!

Demon
among Demons.

NAÏVE, you
can be gifted,
jazzy, smart,
poor, rich,
living ritzy,
you can be a
king, a queen,
strung out on
crack cocaine,
smoking at
your castle,
your friend's
castle!

Strung-Out
on the streets,
up in the crack
house, in a
hotel, motel,
spending
cash, going
for broke
chasing your
fantasies, from
hells deep!

Curious,
you may or
may not live
to see another
sunrise, sunset,
ill none the
less, you'll
Wanna a hit!

Despite of
the Warning
Signs! The
sweating, it's
all about that
hit!

Chancing the
possibility
of having
a STROKE,
a cardiac
arrest.

From hell's
deep, can't
speak, *Shhh*,
don't wanna
be heard,
silence keeps.

From hell's
deep! It's
PARANIOA,
a chronic
form of
insanity.

From hell's
deep, it's
PSYCHOSIS,
it's moon
madness
from smoking
the *Devil's*
aphrodisiac,
CRACK
COCAINE.

From Hell's Deep!

OPEN MIC

PROSE N POETRY

· CHAPTER 14 ·

COCAINE

You wanna feel
the POWER of
CPC, Crack
and Powder
Cocaine?

Before you
snort, take
a hit, spike,
you should
know!

Snorting
or smoking
60% or 3.9 %
Cocaine.

You're playing
the game of
CHANCE
with some
life stinging
CHEMICALS,
capable of
mudding
your thoughts,
capable of
buying your
SOUL!

Their names?
Acetone,
Ammonia,
Benzene,
Ether, Ethyl,
Gasoline,
Hydrogen
Chloride,
Kerosene,
Ketone,
Methyl,
Methane,
Sodium
Hydroxide.

And Sulfuric
Acid. The
Fire of Hell!

When these
CHEMICALS
come together
and poison
your mind
and vital
organs.

Your world as
you know it,
is coming
to ruin.

You want
that long
lasting
feeling
with Crack
and Powder
Cocaine?

Go Ahead!
Roll the Dice!

SNAKE EYES

Looking at Ya!

HARD DRUGS,
A REALITY
OF PAIN!

The illicit, the
wicked.

LISTEN*!*
The hard
drugs
out there!

Know this*!*
When you
cross the
line with
one. And
your passion
for it becomes
excessive, to
the point of
becoming
wild and
unrestrained.

It is then
that you
can believe
your drug of
choice is about
to become your
FEARED and
most hated
ENEMY.

In six months,
you'll be
dreaming of,
and feening
for your new
found friends,
that hard drug,
and alcohol.

Barely holding
on to your
faith! From
a humble
beginning
whence you
came.

You'll go from
having control
of your life to
losing control
inside of two
years.

More than
enough time
for you to
look back
and realize
you been had.

Enough time
for you to
know that
you're a
functional
addict.

Holding down
a 9-to-5,
a career,
a business,
a hustle,
the perfect
marriage,
the perfect
relationship.

The perfect
way of living
coming to
an end.

While your
TONGUE lay
silent with
secrets of you
courting the
illicit, the
WICKED!

LISTEN!
When the
curtain comes
up? Your
secret won't
be a secret
anymore.

What's in the
dark, and in
the shadows,
will come into
the light.

Your actions,
your heavy
drinking and
drugging will
expose you to
the world!

Troubling
events, of
your own
making.

Exposing your
name and
picture over
the internet,
radio, and
TV, in the
newspapers,
and tabloid
magazines.

Breaking News,
finding you
dead or alive.

Going into a
rehab, news
of you living
on the streets,
hustling
aluminum
cans, and
glass, to
feed your
addiction.

News of you
doing time
behind the
illicit, the
wicked!

OPEN MIC

PROSE N POETRY

CHAPTER 16

THE BODY CRIES OUT!

O Mind!

We're in deep
trouble, I
took a bite
out of evil.

The taste of
iniquity has
cast a dark
shadow over
my head.

My apatite
for this
drug, is
testing us.

And you
O Mind,
have a cross
to bear!

Mind you,
O Body!
We're both
guilty!

You and I
know we're
the *Devil's* envy.

His dislike of
us, since day
one of our
creation, he's
spared no
attempts in
alluring us
to his poison.

The Soul
Cries Out!
Hell, I fear!
O Mind!
O Body!

REPENT!
Make amends
for our sins.

OPEN MIC

PROSE N POETRY

CHAPTER 17

O USER!

Remember
the day you
tried that
hard drug?

That was the
day your world
turned gray.

Today, that look
in your eyes,
your peace of
mind, is dying.
Your world is
insane, you're
wishing your
cravings, and
the memories
of them would
just go away,
vanish, never
to be felt, or
thought of
again, ever!

O User,
WISHING
won't help
you!

If you don't
let it go!
Darkness
and what
follows is

certain.

A living death
experienced
by millions.

Like you,
they fell in
love with the
dope, too.

You see were
the drugs and
booze got 'em,
got you!

Your lack of
determination
to CHANGE
to bring this
lifestyle to
an end.

O User!
YOU FAIL!

Your name,
health, wealth,
the material
things, the life
you cherish, will
become sand
gone with
the wind

OPEN MIC

PROSE N POETRY

CHAPTER 18

CAN YOU SAY NO?

No! To the Dope!?

If you're having
a tough time
being strong,
you're weak!

Acknowledge
that your
addiction is
a disease, that
lingers in your
mind, where it
spreads like
cancer, setting
your mind
and you up
for destruction.

Say "NO" to
the Dope.

OPEN MIC

PROSE N POETRY

CHAPTER 19

TEENS

Kids, 12-13
thru 19. Let's
have a REAL
conversation.
These are going
to be the most
challenging,
eye-opening
years of your
life. To be a
CHAMPION!

Strive to be
drug and
alcohol free,
seek real
knowledge,
truth, respect
yourself,
and others.

Respect is
an ASSET.
The TRUTH
will set you
FREE.

QUESTION!
Are you
defiant,
a rebel, a
songbird
in the nest,
chirping loudly?

Game for
Vampires,
and Wolves,
fighting to get
your attention!

Demanding your
awareness of
their crafty
ways and
invites!

Are you angry,
cause of your
parents dislike
of your toxic
ways and
toxic friends?

Listen!
Running with
them, you'll
become a
victim, with
a fifty-fifty
chance, you'll
windup dirty.

No need to
be angry with
your parents,
with your
siblings, and
friends who
care, they're
only looking
out for you.

Fighting with
them is a sign
of you running
away from
home to that
AMORAL
universe?

Your parents
biggest fear,
with all the
devilry going
on out there!

No one in
that dark
world cares,
they're too
busy with
themselves.

You'll need
more than
a couple
dollars and
temper
tantrums
to survive it.

You're smart,
and you know
you can't
always have
it your way!

Right or Wrong?
Thinking that
you can, is
how babies
in the woods
wind up being
a TARGET.
A prize catch,
in Old Nick's
game.

That's active
with drug
dealers, and
kerb crawlers,
tricksters and
traffickers
looking to
cash in on
a runaway
teen, running
straight to
the *Devil's*
playground.

To Old Nick
disguised as
a friend to
take you in,
with a plan
to push you
deeper into
the abyss.

Into the arms
of Vampires,
and Wolves
promising
you a Castle
in Spain.

LIES that'll
blind you.
Your worse
nightmare
is coming.

LISTEN*!*
Old Nick
and his crew.
They're into
drugging
and sex
trafficking.

How do you
go around 'em?

(1). Choose your
female and
male friends
wisely.

(2). Part ways with
that I don't
care attitude!
It'll cause you
to error, loose
your way.

(3). Under no
circumstances
do you accept
Old Nick's
candy from
a friend, a
stranger,
from a
family member.

(4). Value your
health, your
originality,
your freedom.

(5). Stay vigilant
24/7.

OPEN MIC

PROSE N POETRY

CHAPTER 20

YOUNG AND DYING

Dying from a
drug overdose,
from alcohol
poisoning,
from gun
violence,
dying over
colors, over
material things.

Young and
dying to do
time in prison
for the cash,
for the
streets to
welcome
them with
this phrase!

"Everybody else
is doing it!"

Dying to see
what's on
the other
side of that
black tinted
glass.

The tip of
the blade
lifestyle,
that ends in
a bad dream.

Darkness covers
their eyes.

MISLEAD!
They're living
and dying
for what's
on the other
side of that
black tinted
glass!

It's madness
with little
chances of
surviving it!

With little
chances of
living in
peace and
harmony.

Young and
Dying. It's
Not Cool!

OPEN MIC

PROSE N POETRY

CHAPTER 21

IT'S NOT COOL!

It's not cool
giving in,
giving up,
closing the
book on
yourself!

It's not cool
to end your
hopes and
dreams, cause
you failed
twenty times
or more.

Get back in
the fight!

Drinking and
drugging
won't help
you WIN.

You're going
down the
rabbit's hole
with this one
for sure.

It's not cool to
deny REALITY,
in the fact that
you can DIE!

From partying,
from drinking
and drugging
while driving,
from a deadly
disease with
your name
on it. From
a suicide,
a homicide.

It's Not Cool!

Ruining your
life, your
good name
for a POOR
reputation
that exceeds
shame.

It's Not COOL!

OPEN MIC

PROSE N POETRY

CHAPTER 22

FAKE FRIENDS

Fakers, the
pretenders,
they're the
most dicey,
unpredictable
kind of friends
you can associate
with.

They'll grin
in your face,
backbite you,
use you, they'll
trip you up!

They'll do a
hatchet job
on ya' they
could give
a red cent,
about you.

They don't
like you,
love you,
they pretend
that they do!

Fake friends
they envy
you! They're
jealous of
you!

When they
come around
they're smiling,
zigzagging.

It's a good
thing, not
a sad thing
when you
stop embracing
'em.

You're saving
your neck
from a
vipers bite.

Loyal friends.
You can trust
MORALITY.

You can
trust God.

Real friends
won't do
you wrong.

Fake friends,
after using
you again,
they'll call
you up
later, and
ask you for
another favor.

It's about
the good
DEED
you did.

The ACTS
of generosity.

Showing
appreciation
is something
fake friends
are naïve to.

They're illusive.
They'll have
you swearing!

FAKE friends,
they're your
FRENEMIES,
not your
friend.

OPEN MIC

PROSE N POETRY

CHAPTER 23

BULLIES EVERYWHERE

Bullies they're
everywhere,
hot-tempered,
ego tripping,
itching for
a victim.

Looking for
someone to
bullyrag, to
harass. Looking
to ruin your
day, your life.

You'll find these
intoxicated
egotist, self-
conceited
mortals were
they breathe.

In the workplace,
in cyber space
in buildings
of worship,
in the schools,
homes, in your
neighborhood,
in your village.

You'll discover
BULLIES
doing what
they do best,
testing the
lionhearted,
the cowards,
the helpless,
the powerless.

Crossing the
holy line, testing
God with their
belittling
language
and lies.

Out there
stirring evil
up, causing
tempers to flare.
YELLING their
way or the
highway!

Being arrogant
and dramatic
about it!

Watch out
BULLIES, in
time your
vanity will
glisten, and
you, you'll
have a dark
story to tell.

It'll be a
page turner!

OPEN MIC

PROSE N POETRY

CHAPTER 24

ARE YOU NEGLECTING YOUR EDUCATION?

Age fifteen-
thru-nineteen.
Playing hooky
from school,
drinking,
and drugging.

You're not
thinking
about the
worse, that
can happen!

You could end
up Expelled,
OD'ing,
Deranged,
in Jail.

Prior to you
taking this
washed-out
ROAD.

You and millions
of teens gave
thought to
flirting with
alcohol and
a hard drug
ONCE.

Today! You
and millions
of teens are
dropping out
of school for
a high!

Tomorrow
you'll be
standing
under the
streetlights,
chasing *Diablo's*
way of life.

Once Curious*!*
You're not curious
anymore, you
have experience
getting high,
experience
neglecting
your education.

Naïve come
up to speed
with this
knowledge.

Being under
the influence
of a drug. You're
setting yourself
up to go deep in
your feelings
when you take
that drink!

That will inspire
you through
Diablo feeding
on your emotions,
on your reactions
from the alcohol
and chemicals.

That'll have you
believing in
what you're
doing, feeling
and hearing!

Your demons,
enticing you to
entice a friend,
a stranger to
get high.

Inspired by
your demons,
you're about
to RUIN their
life!

15 thru 19
neglecting
your education,
come age 20-24.

No DIPLOMA!
You're a NON-
ACHIEVER
wasting your
TALENTS away
drinking and
drugging.

Chasing *Diablo's*
way of life!

Tonight, you'll
be sleeping
under the
streetlights,
experiencing
the school of
hard knocks.

OPEN MIC

PROSE N POETRY

CHAPTER 25

CANNABIS'
THE TRUTH

One of the
greatest gifts
bestowed upon
humankind is
the *Cannabis*
plant.

Its place of
origin is
Central Asia.

One of its
known
aliases is
Marijuana.

Cannabis was
not created
to cause
ALARM!

Its creation is
unlike cotton,
fossil fuels,
and trees.

Cannabis is
UNEEK. It
comes with
unlimited
ASSETS!

Renewable
energy, biofuel,
oil, rope, and
much more.

When things
was going
great with
Cannabis in
the old days.

In 1619, in
Jamestown
Colony, VA.
US Farmers
were ordered
to grow
Cannabis,
Hemp, or
go to Jail.

This law was
enforced in
Massachusetts
in 1631, and in
Connecticut
1632.

During the
16th, 17th and
18th centuries,
Cannabis was
GOLD!

Born out of
a conspiracy
in the 19th
century.

MARIJUANA
brainwashing,
was too much
for the mind,
eyes, and ears
to believe!

Propagandist
cooked up a
pork pie that
capitalized on
black market
theatrics that
made billions
associating
Cannabis with
Xenophobia,
and Crimes.

Their ungodly
attacks ruined
Cannabis'
good name
and reputation.

On, August
2nd 1937,
The Marijuana
Tax Act was
enacted.

On, October
1, 1937, the
first arrest
and conviction
for marijuana
possession
became law.

This law put
the squeeze on
Cannabis, making
it impossible
for cannabis
to compete
with cotton
coal, oil,
trees, and
opioids.

Worth hundreds
of BILLIONS
of dollars to
its competitors.

33 years past!
Billions WON
the case for
passing the
Controlled
Substance
Act of 1970.
Classifying
Cannabis as a
Schedule I drug.

A menace to
society, beaten
by fiction, the
competition, and
the Marijuana
Tax Act.

Since 1906,
1937, 2018.

112 years of
propaganda.

Millions were
imprisoned
for farming,
selling, and
for possessing
Cannabis for
recreational
use.

The Good News*!*
On, December
the 13th, 2018,
The powers-
that-be signed
the Hemp Farm
Bill into Law.

It's a bit late,
but on time.

This level of
motivation
puts *Cannabis*,
Hemp, back
in its rightful
place, in the
HEART of
COMMERCE.

OPEN MIC

PROSE N POETRY

CHAPTER 26

HEMP OR
BLACK GOLD?

Long before
industrialists
launched
black gold,
HEMP was
number one
on the Charts!

For better or
worse! Two oil
pioneers came
along and
changed those
dynamics.

Drake & Sweeny
SHOOK up the
world in the
cruddiest
way!

They cashed in
on Crude Oil.

Drake hit a
lick at 69.5
feet deep.

The FIRST in
the world to
extract black
gold in Venango
County, PA, on
August 27, 1859.

That year, he
sold 2000
barrels, the
following year,
1860, 500,000.

Dreamt of being
wealthy, Drake
succeeded in
the oil business.

Oil Barons,
bankers,
visionaries,
developers,
entrepreneurs,
and investors
their Earthly
dreams got
BIGGER!

Enthusiasm and
greed filled the
air. There were
BILLIONS, and
land to be had,
castles, and
mansions to
build.

Seven years
later, 1866, the
world witnessed
Mr. Sweeny's
invention!

"An Improved
Rotary Rock
Boring Machine."

That, in January
11, 1901, on
Spindletop Hill,
drilling for Texas
Tea in the town
of Beaumont,
Texas, above
a Salt Dome,
sent up a
GUSHER!

This invention
sent oil drillers,
steelmakers,
automobile,
aircraft, trains,
planes, and
shipbuilders
to MONEY
heaven.

Along the way,
blinded by their
inventions, their
material riches,
their diesel and
gas guzzling
vehicles.

They didn't
foresee the
oil spills, the
threats to the
Sea, the black
smoke and smog
polluting the air!

You couldn't
breathe in the
1950s, 60s. In
the 21st century,
investors are
banking on
black gold,
and coal.

The trapped
heat in the
atmosphere
is our biggest
THREAT!

Flash floods,
wildfires,
monsoons,
hurricanes,
and tornadoes
are gassing up.

Sizzling HOT
summers are
melting the
blue ice into
the deep, the sea
level is rising.

The Antarctica,
the Himalayas
and Greenland
ice sheet are
leaving our
sights forever.

QUESTIONING
our addiction to
bankrolling our
own Reckoning!

Climate changing,
global warming,
and greenhouse
gases, is wrecking
the planet.

As we look on
in disbelief,
asking ourselves,
is this the end
of our world!?!

Gabriel's Trumpet
is blowing!

Time for
redemption,
time to atone
for the bulldust
that threw HEMP
under the bus
in the way of
corruption.

Solving our
problems! The
Hemp Industry
can monetize
it, reap the
RICHES of
Solomon.
Preserving
Mother Earth.

Without her,
MONEY
serves for
NO benefit.

No time to
waste. End of
the Stories!
End of the
Quarrelling's!

Hemp or
Black Gold?

OPEN MIC

PROSE N POETRY

CHAPTER 27

BILLIONS
PLUS-PLUS

As the world
turns, millions
are investing
billions in
the most
ghastly events
of all times.

Millions are
investing
billions in
crimes, in
weapons of
mass destruction.

In killer drugs
and human
organs.

You read it
right, in
human
ORGANS.

Millions are
investing
billions in
the most
GHASTLY
events of all
times!

You got the
puppet masters
stalking the
strays and
runaways.

Pulling their
strings, selling
their minds,
bodies and
souls to the
highest bidder,
to the fat cats,
and wolves in
sheep's clothing.

As the world
turns! It's about
business, not
feelings, the
business could
give a rap song
about the three
blind mice!

Who's investing
their OWN
money into
the most
ghastly events
of all times.

In a fool's
paradise, in
homelessness,
in homeless

adults, young
adults, children,
in homeless
teens, in
hunger, in
crowded
morgues,
and prisons,
in addiction.

Look around you!

Millions are
investing
BILLIONS
into the most
ghastly events
of all times.

OPEN MIC

PROSE N POETRY

CHAPTER 28

SO, YOU WANNA BE A DRUG DEALER?

You wanna put
some work in
for some of
those billions?
You want-a
million, ten?

Ambitious!
To whom this
may, concern:

Bold, daring,
if you dare
to brave
Gehenna.

You hit-and
-miss, you
pay the piper.

Aiming high,
keep in mind,
those speedy
profits you
make will
come back
and bankrupt
you.

In the form of
a wireless bug,
an informant,
snitch, in the
form of envy
and jealousy,
in the form of
a big or little
mistake you'll
make.

Just know!
For whatever
beneficial or
weak reason
you RISK
your life and
freedom for is
of no concern
to the court.

It's about the
lives you've
destroyed,
even yours.

So, before you
choose this dark
ego, ask yourself
these two questions?

1). Do I wanna die young?

2). Spend years in prison,
dreaming and
reminiscing?

To whom this
may, concern:
If you dare
to brave this
calling, this
is as real
as it gets.

The day you
get busted,
bailed out,
or no bail.

You'll sit in
the County
Jail for a
minute.

Found Guilty,
you're on
your way
to a place,
off the path
of civilization.

Now a felon,
living the
prison life,
following
commands,
rules, and
regulations
24/7.

No home
cooked meals,
restaurant,
or fast food
for years!

FIRST timer
you're on the
scene were
extortion,
foul play,
dirty deeds,
drugs, and
groomers
are never late
on claiming
their targeted
PREY!

Young, and
vulnerable
you're bought
and sold
without your
consent!

Only two
ways to go,
self-control
or bisexual!

So, you Wanna
be a drug
dealer!?
Can you
do time, 10,
25, 30 years,
life in prison?

Going in BROKE!
Reexamine
your thinking,
the first 365
days won't
be easy, and
thereafter,
either.

The years, life
behind those
walls, and
razor wire
fences,
guarantees it.

When reality
sets in, you'll
ask yourself
often, was
making a
deal with
the *Devil*
worth it,
getting 10,
25, 30 years,
life in prison!

YOUNG,
facing old age
behind bars.

To whom this
may, concern:

If you dare
to brave this
calling, this
is as real
as it gets.

OPEN MIC

PROSE N POETRY

CHAPTER 29

THE SAGA OF A RICH DRUG LORD

HER SUCCESS, HER DOWNFALL!

This ambitious
young lady
worked hard!
She didn't
have two
nickels to
rub together
after taking care
of the rent, bills,
herself, and her
two siblings.

Tired of being
broke! She
imagined
herself being
wealthy.

Determined to
win against
POVERTY.

The chance to
fulfill her desire
dropped by to
say hello. They
offered her a
hand up, a
zero down
deal on one
hundred

Ki's with
the help of
moving it.

The cash cow
she wished for!
She signed her
name in blood,
sold her soul
to *Lucifer.*

In the world
of pleasure
and pain, she
was the players
choice, picked
by the ladies
and gents
with the
deep pockets.

Celebrating her
SUCCESS.

At her private
parties, in the
company of
TALENT,
beautiful
faces, and
distinguished
smiles.

She'd serve
Caviar Galilee,
horderves,
and the most
expensive
champagne,
and wine.

Promoting
her BRAND
to expand,
she'd spread
soft white
lines upon
the looking
glass.

Five years in
the game,
greasing
the palms
of crooked
officials. Her
sales grew by
the millions.
SAVVY, she
owned gold,
silver, and
businesses,
that paid taxes.

Her new home
was a luxury
villa, sitting
on 40 acres of
oceanic land,
with a glorious
view of the
mountains,
white sand,
and blue
water beaches.

Wealth, and
a paradise she
shared with
her siblings,
and Gypsy
Vanner horses.

She was into
charities,
classic cars
and custom
Hogs,
showpieces.

She drove
BENTLEY,
in the air, a
Learjet, and
Eurocopter,
stationed on
her mega yacht.
SUSSCCESS

She dreamed
of being wealthy,
she wined and
dined wherever
in the world
she liked!

Her ideal
fragrance was

Clive Christian
No. 1

Her fashions,
leather, suede,
Levi Jeans,
Kobe sneakers,
Valentino,
Dolce, and
Gucci gators.

Her jewelry
was CUSTOM
designed.

She lived a
life of luxury.
Under the
radar, for
35 years.

Until she
heard that
two Canaries
sung her name.

She was in
the eagle's eyes.

She planned
for the day
they would
come for her.

She salvaged
her patents,
paid her
taxes, sold
the estate
and her prize
winning horses.

Not too long
after the big
sale, they jailed
her on a drug
trafficking
charge.

Her first offense.

An unhappy
ending that
took some
singing, and
millions in
CASH!

She escaped
death's hand,
did ten, time
served.

FREE, now
a parolee,
living in the
SOUTHEAST
with a book
and movie
deal in the
making.

All you
ENROLLIES
now you see

from a birdies
beak, tweet-
tweet!

You see 'em
going up,
and coming
down with
the help of
loose lips.

PLAYERS!
The DICE are
rolling!

In closing,
this is The Saga
of a Rich Drug
Lord. Her
Success, Her
Downfall.

Short-lived,
like a high are
the fortunes
that come
and go with
the risk!

Short-lived,
like a high
is the taste
of milk and
honey in this
game.

OPEN MIC

PROSE N POETRY

CHAPTER 30

IT'S TIME
TO SAY GOODBYE!

It's time for
you to shut the
partying down!

You've been
courting with
self-destruction
for too long,
and what have
you achieved?
Nothing but
heartaches!

How many
great people,
and great
names have
you known
and heard of,
who used and
abused a hard
drug! Who was
eager to see
their dreams
being fulfilled
tomorrow,
but their
tomorrow
never came.

Death showed
up instead,
blaming the
user, for
ignoring the
threats, that
sinking feeling
that something
bad is happening
to Ya! SCARING
YOU!

It's a wake-up call!

What's your
name? It's
time say
goodbye to
getting high.

You've been
courting with
self-destruction
for too long!

OPEN MIC

PROSE N POETRY

· CHAPTER 31 ·

AS THIS IMPLIES

It's time to
revolutionize.
Time to engage
in a fight for
your peace
of mind.

If you're
facing losses,
and setbacks
on account of
you getting
high.

As This Implies!

It's time to
revolutionize,
time to engage
in a fight for
your life.

OPEN MIC

PROSE N POETRY

CHAPTER 32

IT'S NOT
AN ATTITUDE
IT'S THE WAY!

Life in the
21st century ~

TO SURVIVE IT!

Don't toy
around with
hard drugs.

You should
feel threaten,
by 'em!

Terrified of
fentanyl, and
zai-luh-zeen,
the zombie
drug.

You should
be terrified
of riding
the white
horse, of
meth, crack,
old school
caviar,
candy, rock,
synthetic drugs.

You should
feel threatened
by 'em!

Saying No!
Refusing
to party
with 'em!

It's Not An
Attitude It's
The Way ~

OPEN MIC

PROSE N POETRY

CHAPTER 33

THE WARNING SIGNS!

Spiritually,
you can feel
your SOUL
slipping into
darkness.

You can feel
that alcohol
and drug
bringing
you bad luck!

Your negative
outlook on life
shows through
your actions,
your skin color
is changing;
a warning
sign!

Trying to hide it!?

The yellow in
your eyes,
is an Omen,
a warning
sign!

You're mind
and body is
poisoned,
the poison is
taking over.

Your drinking
and drugging,
your addiction,
your emotional
and physical pain
is alarming!

You're knocking
on Hell's door.

The Warning Signs!

Telling you,
you're your
own worst
enemy.

OPEN MIC

PROSE N POETRY

CHAPTER 34

GETTING HIGH!

Getting stoned for
the first time?

First Timer!
You think
you're safe
from addiction?
You're Not!

After your first
experiment with
an alcoholic,
beverage, with
a hard drug
you'll feel
grown for
a day!

Young and
naïve, this
won't be
your, last
high! You
just bought
yourself
another round.

You need to
know what's
coming next!

These FACTS!
That second,
third, fourth,
fifth, sixth,

and seventh,
high, will
take you
there, to
a life of
drinking,
and drugging.

TWO years
from now,
you'll be
regretting
you ever
indulged
in alcohol
and drugs.

What's Ahead!?
Heart-Breaking
news blowing
up your name
and picture
on a Missing
Persons, and
Most Wanted
Poster, on your
Mugshot, your
Obituary.

Life-altering
changes giving
you a glimpse
into what the
future holds
for you!

You're one
step away
from that
place in
time we're
talking about,
hell on earth.

That eighth
high, will take
you there!

Going for nine?
You're spending
your money
as if there's no
tomorrow, no
responsibilities
for you to
bear!

Going for ten!
Your living
hell is fast
approaching.

Your social,
and financial
ruin.

Spiritual
warfare, conflicts
of interest with
Self!

The CAVING
in of your
self-esteem,
your intellect.
Your living
hell revealing
itself.

Drinking and
Drugging!
How low
can you go?

DEGRADATION
LOW!

OPEN MIC

PROSE N POETRY

CHAPTER 35

SELF-INCARCERATION

What are the
ODDS of you
doing a long
stretch in a
mental prison
of your own
making!?

What are the
odds of you
being enticed
by whisky,
wine, hard
drugs, sex,
and money?

Snares the
likes of an
ANACONDA,
hurrying to
squeeze its
prey.

You're odds
of sinking
from grace!?

Doing time
in a mental
prison of
your own
making,
are as great
as anyone
else's.

OPEN MIC

PROSE N POETRY

CHAPTER 36

TIME FOR
A CHANGE

What's your name?

It's time for
you to end
your love
affair with
your demons.

It's time to
stop laying
the blame on
your past,
on your
failures.

You can
blame it on
your abuse
of that hard
drug, beer,
whisky, and
wine.

Hold yourself
accountable,
one, and all
sin. You're
an addict,
the most
painful of
what you've
become!

A slave to that
hard drug,
and alcohol,
to that feeling
you can't let
go of.

What's your name?

It's time to
pull the plug.

OPEN MIC

PROSE N POETRY

CHAPTER 37

OUT AND ABOUT

Hard Drugs,
and synthetic
drugs of all kinds
are out and about
downtown,
up-town.

Out and about
on the northside,
westside, eastside,
on the deep
southside of
town.

Out and about
chopping it up
in the rurales,
in the suburbs,
up in the hills,
down in the
valley's below,
chopping it up!

Hard drugs and
synthetic drugs
of all kinds are
showing up,
and showing
out in your
neighborhood,
city, hometown,
showing up
and showing
out!

Curious?
Come Closer!
With these
drugs out
and about!

Don't go out
and get
MISLED,
lead up
hell's path.

Trust, it's not
the path you
Wanna be on!

OPEN MIC

PROSE N POETRY

CHAPTER 38

DESIGNER DRUGS

Hundreds of 'em
invented in
underground
laboratories.

Designed to mimic
the cannabis, coca,
and opium plants,
and other plant,
and chemical
based drugs.

Designed to
amuse, to ease
the pain, designed
to make you feel
superhuman,
phenomenal,
designer drugs!

Designed to trip
you up!

Their history
gained notorious
status in the
18, 19, and
20th centuries.

In those days it
was Amphetamine,
Heroin, Morphine,
Orange Sunshine,
Purple Haze, LSD,
XTC, Angel Dust,
Black Mollies,
Cocaine, and
Crack Cocaine.

Designer Drugs
are born
every day,
coming out
a thousand
times stronger.

Designed to
trip you up!

OPEN MIC

PROSE N POETRY

CHAPTER 39

DRUGS THAT KILL!

FENTANYL,
TRANQ,
Oxi-Rust,
the alien of
crack cocaine.

Out there with
Scopolamine,
the *Devil's*
BREATH*!*

With meth,
Rohypnol,
Krokodil,
heaven and
hell, spice,
synthetic
cannabis,
bath salt.

With DXM,
Demerol,
Dilaudid,
Percocet,
OxyContin,
Vicodin, and
Oxymorphone.

HELLO*!*
It's Murder 8,
Oxy 80, Pain
Killers,
Ms. Emma,
KILLING 'EM.

OPEN MIC

PROSE N POETRY

CHAPTER 40

TOXIC COCKTAILS

In the bloody
mix, you have
cocaine, and
heroin.

An upper and
a downer, a
death sentence,
playing out
when mixed,
snorted, or
injected into
the blood
stream.

Which, upon
impact, the
heroin slows
down your
breathing,
the cocaine
speeds up
your heartbeat!
Beats racing
faster than light.

SPEED-BALLING!

In the bloody
mix are cocaine
and heroin.

Spinning the
chamber,
playing a
deadly game
of Russian
roulette.

Ten minutes of
pure heaven,
they say!

You're looking
into the eyes
of the angel
of death.

You inject
this deadly
cocktail into
your blood
stream, and
the high takes
a deadly turn
for the worst!

May your soul
rest in peace.

OPEN MIC

PROSE N POETRY

CHAPTER 41

IT DOESN'T MATTER ABOUT YOUR SOCIOECONIMIC STATUS

Rich, Middle-
Class, Poor!

Passing time
amusing
oneself,
drinking,
and drugging.

You're in a
dark place,
about to go
bankrupt.

It doesn't
matter about
your social-
economic status.

Educated,
Uneducated.

This game
Ain't biased,
it sales to
anybody!

Passing time
drinking and
drugging.

The WEAKEST
thought you
can think of
is thinking,
you have
control over
a controlled
substance.

You got deep
pockets?!

The deeper!

The harder it
is to govern
your addiction.

Of which every
addict on the
social economic
ladder wishes
at this very
moment!

They could
TERMINATE
their cravings.

Wishing they
could turn
back the
hands of time!

You can be a
loving parent,
a retiree, a
superstar,
straight A's
student,
famous in
your job.

Look up one
day and find
yourself pre-
occupied with
a pill, with
a hard drug,
and a hard
drink.

It doesn't
matter about
your social-
economic
status.

The Devil
whispers
SOFTLY!

Are you
craving?
Jonesing?

Time to get
CLEAN!

This move
takes courage.
You got to
get some.

No time to
waste!

It doesn't
matter about
your social-
economic
status.

OPEN MIC

PROSE N POETRY

CHAPTER 42

RELAPSE!

Five years
CLEAN*!*

You had to
pop that pill
didn't you?

You had to
go, and spike,
take a hit,
a snort,
a drink,
one, two,
too many.

RELASPE!
Your monsters
from hell are
back, and
you're in
DENAIL!

Saying you're
sober, but
you're not.
Lying to
yourself, to
your family.

RELASPE!
Your monsters
from hell
are back!

With some
stressful and
unexpected
events waiting
for ya'

RELASPE!
Your demon
from hell
is back!

OPEN MIC

PROSE N POETRY

CHAPTER 43

LISTEN TO THESE GREAT CLASSICS!

We Fall Down

(2) Donnie McClurkin | We Fall Down lyrics - YouTube

James Brown
King Heroin
Eric Clapton
Cocaine

Curtis Mayfield
Pusherman
Steppenwolf
Pusherman

John Lennon &
Yoko Ono
Cold Turkey

Gil Scott Heron
Angel Dust
The Bottle

The Dramatics
The Devil Is Dope

**Michael Jackson
Make, That Change**

**And this, 1971 Classic!
Smiling Faces Sometimes**

"Beware of the handshake
that hides a Snake."
"The impossible task
is to figure out,
which of the
SMILES is
a mask."

More Classic Drug Songs

https://en.wikipedia.org/wiki/User:Astanhope/List_of_Song_about_Drugs

Category: Songs about drugs - Wikipediahttp://en.wikipedia.org/wiki/User:Sasquatch/List_of_songs_about_drugs

http://rateyourmusic.com/list/djorkaeff/mojos_the_100_greatest_drug_songs_ever/

https://en.wikipedia.org/wiki/List_of_drug_films

IN LOVING MEMORY
AND DEDICATION

To the casualties, to the genius, savvy,
funny, and hilarious.

Gone, but never forgotten.

R.I.P.

http://en.wikipedia.org/wiki/List_of_drug-related_deaths

OPEN MIC

PROSE N POETRY

CHAPTER 45

PRAY

God is the
Author of Life,
the Inventor
of time.

How you
choose to
spend your
life and time,
doing good or
evil to yourself,
to others.

Your actions
and dealings!
Nothing is
hidden.

God is The
All Seeing.

The All Hearing
of a floating
feather, of
motion in
the deepest
depths of
the oceans.

The All-Hearing
of prayers.

Pray
O Lord of the
Magnificent
Throne.

I beg of Thee
forgiveness
for my past
and recent
sins.

O Lord!
I ask of Thee
a faith that
will engage
my time,
talent, and
efforts, in
making a
difference.

O Lord!
Give me
Victory over
evil, and not
its success
over me.

O Lord!
Bring out the
best in me,
cause me to
trust Thee,
to rely upon
Thee.

O Lord!
Prepare me
for life's
journeys.

Inspire me
to remember
Thee, for
the heart
and spirit
Thou instilled
in me.

O Lord!
I seek Thy
help, and
thy guidance.

I seek shelter
in Thee, from
the evil of
that which
the wind
bringeth.

Amen

OPEN MIC

PROSE N POETRY

CHAPTER 46

THOUGHTS FOR TODAY!

If you tried a hard drug,
and you didn't like the high!
You're a shining star! You are!
If you're using a hard drug,
and you're enjoying the high!

You're the unfortunate one,
soon to be a slave
to Apollyon in
a dark game,
that presents
itself in a very
elusive light.

A life of
disillusionment,
the confessions
of a regrettable end.

OPEN MIC

PROSE N POETRY

CHAPTER 47

GET YOUR FACTS IN REAL TIME!

INTERNATIONAL CRIME AND DRUG REPORTS
https://www.unodc.org/unodc/index.html
https://www.unodc.org/unodc/en/data-and-analysis/statistics/index.html
https://www.unodc.org/unodc/en/data-and-analysis/statistics/corruption.html
https://dataunodc.un.org
https://www.interpol.int/en
https://www.independent.co.uk/topic/drugs
https://www.euronews.com/tag/drug-trafficking

THE NATIONAL INSTITUTE ON DRUG ABUSE
https://www.drugabuse.gov/international/news

OPEN MIC

PROSE N POETRY

CHAPTER 48

REAL TIME OPPORTUITIES

Cannabis, Hemp, and
New Developments.

Stay on Top of the Latest
Cannabis News, Stocks,
Inventions, Forecast,
Predictions, and
Entrepreneurial Opportunities.

**At SDK Hunter
Consultant Group
(SDK Hunter LLC)**
www.sdkhunter.com
www.marketwatch.com
https://hemptoday.net
www.benzinga.com
www.newcannabisventures.com

Connect with Henry Ford and Rudolf Diesel.
Sharing a common interest in Hemp,
and BIODGRDABLE fuel.

What is the proprietary VALUE of
the Cannabis, Coca, and Opium plants?

Their value will prove superior to that of GOLD and SILVER. When global
economic disparity is no more.
When the cannabis, coca, and opium plants
are manage with complete and focused
attention to preventing severe damage to
the environment to mental health, to freedom.

OPEN MIC

PROSE N POETRY

CHAPTER 49

LET'S GET STARTED

QUESTION, WHAT DOES CANNABIS, HEMP, HAVE IN COMMON WITH THESE FOUR SCIENTISTS AND INNOVATERS?

Mr. George Washington Carver, Mr. Henry Ford, Mr. Thomas Edison, and Mr. Rudolf Diesel?

ANSWER, THE CHEMURGIC MOVEMENT

Please see https://ushempmuseum.us and

GEORGE WASHINGTON CARVER, AND HENRY FORD "IN THE MEETING OF THE MINDS"

http://www.youtube.com/watch?v=Ackz1ILVYTU

HENRY FORD AND GEORGE WASHINGTON CARVER PIONEERS OF ZERO WASTE
by John Ferrell

https://www.scribd.com/document/206111318/George-Washington-Carver-and-Henry-Ford-Pioneers-of-Zero-Waste

INTRODUCTION TO MR. GEORGE WASHINGTON CARVER

http://en.wikipedia.org/wiki/George_Washington_Carver

MR. HENRY FORD http://en.wikipedia.org/?title=henry_Ford

MR. THOMAS EDISON https://en.wikipedia.org/wiki/Thomas_Edison

AND MR. RUDOLF DIESEL https://en.wikipedia.org/wiki/Rudolf_Diesel

HENRY FORD AND RUDOLF DIESEL FOR BIODEGRADABLE FUEL PARTS I and II.

http://www.youtube.com/watch?v=MGZEMwMx2vk
http://www.youtube.com/watch?v=YR58dWGeBks&feature=related

THE CANNABIS, HEMP REVOLUTION
(386) Hemp revolution - YouTube

OPEN THIS TRESURE CHEST OF
VALUABLE HEMP CONTENT
HEMPOLOGY.ORG - ALL ARTICLES

CANNABIS SCIENCE & RESEARCH
https://jcannabisresearch.biomedcentral.com
www.cannabissciencetech.com
https://scholar.google.com
https://www.springer.com/us
(Search Hemp or Cannabis sativa)
https://cbdoracle.com/news/cannabis-education-training-schools

INDUSTRIAL HEMP
**Earth's Number One Biomass Resource For
Bio Plastic, Energy, Biofuel, Oil, Construction
Materials, Textiles, and much-much more.**

HEMP SOURCES
https://en.wikipedia.org/wiki/Hemp
www.hempgallery.com
www.hemptrade.ca
www.hemphasis.com

THE BENEFITS OF HEMP SEEDS
(641) hemp seeds benefits - YouTube
www.ratical.org/renewables/hempseed1.html

HEMP SEED OIL By Gero Leson
https://www.scribd.com/document/55946056/Hemp-Nutrition

THE FUTURE WITH CANNABIS, HEMP
Banking-Copyrights-Patents-Trade Marks-Formulars-New Discoveries-Technology-Science-Raw Materials-Biomass Fuel-Medical and Nonmedical Products-Manufacturing-Distribution-Imports-Exports.

INDUSTRIAL HEMP AT WORK
(385) hemp building materials - YouTube
(1) hemp plastic - YouTube
Industrial Hemp Solutions - YouTube

MEDICAL CANNBIS
https://en.wikipedia.org/wiki/Medical_cannabis
(641) medical cannabis - YouTube

SERIOUS MINDED ENTREPRENEURS!
INTRESTED IN A BUSINESS DEGREE IN THE CANNABIS, HEMP INDUSTRY? YOUR OWN BRAND, PRIVATE LABEL?
https://www.cannaconnection.com/strains/breeders
www.bulkhempwarehouse.com
www.nanolabshemp.com
https://arborvita8.com
www.hemptech.co.nz
www.hemptraders.com
www.zelfo-technology.com
https://www.businessstudent.com/topics/best-cannabis-course-options

CANNABIS, HEMP, MARKET FORCAST
https://www.grandviewresearch.com/industry-analysis/industrial-hemp-market

INTERNATIONAL CANNABIS,
HEMP SOURCES
hemptoday.net
www.hempplastic.com
Hemp Products Products - ecplaza.net

BIODEGRADABLE PLASTIC!
HEMP CAN MAKE IT HAPPEN
www.bioplasticsmagazine.com
www.plasticstoday.com
www.plasticsnews.com

CANNABIS NEWS
www.cannabisnews.com
http://medicalmarijuana411.com
https://hempindustrydaily.com
https://www.ganjapreneur.com/marijuana-news
https://www.newcannabisventures.com

CANNABIS, HEMP, REASEARCH,
SCIENTIFIC DOCUMENTS
Home - Springer

THE PLANETARY REASONS FOR
GROWING AND PRODUCING HEMP!
HISTORICAL OIL SPILLS AND EXPOLSIONS
(1) historical oil spill gulf of mexico 2010 - YouTube
(1) global oil explosions - YouTube - YouTube

GLOBAL WARMING AND CLIMATE CHANGE
Home – Climate Change: Vital Signs of the Planet (nasa.gov)
www.youtube.com/watch?v=UcWpkWBX04E
(38) environmental pollution - YouTube
(38) flooding across the world - YouTube
(672) deadly tornadoes 2022 - YouTube
Wildfires globally - YouTube
https://public.wmo.int/en
https://unfccc.int

GEOENGINEERING
CHEMWEBS AND CHEMTRAILS
(423) geoengineering - YouTube
(38) chemwebs - YouTube
(38) chemtrails - YouTube

COCA THE DIVINE PLANT OF THE INCAS
Coca www.wikipedia.org/wiki/Coca
Images www.erowid.org/plants/coca

THE GREAT INCA REBELLION
Starring Francisco Pizarro
(38) francisco pizarro documentary - YouTube
And Francisco de Toledo
http://cienciadelacoca.org/CocaSpain.html
(38) francisco de taledo - YouTube

COCA CREATIONS
Coca Wine by Angelo Mariani
http://en.wikipedia.org/wiki/Vin_Mariani
(628) vin mariani wine - YouTube

COCA-COLA!
Invented by Dr. John Stith Pemberton
http://en.wikipedia.org/wiki/Coca-Cola

COCAINE THE FIRST ANSTHESIA
By Albert Niemann, Chemist
https://en.wikipedia.org/wiki/Albert_Niemann_(chemist
And **Sigmund Freud,** a Neurologist by trade was so deeply involved with his work he became **addicted** to **cocaine** while experimenting on various promising discoveries.
www.wikipedia.org/wiki/Sigmund_Freud

Karl Koller An Ophthalmologist.
Focused on **cocaine** medicinal use in **General Anesthesia**
www.wikipedia.org/wiki/Karl_Koller_(ophthalmologist)
www.cocaine.org/karl-koller/index.html

POWDER COCAINE, THE REAL THING*!*
www.erowid.org/chemicals/cocaine/cocaine.shtml
(628) cocaine manufacturing in 2022 - YouTube

FROM HELL'S DEEP, CRACK COCAINE
crack cocaine 1980s - YouTube
(628) crack cocaine 1990s - YouTube

Crack Cocaine in the 21st Century
(628) crack cocaine 2022 - YouTube
(1) crack cocaine destroying lives - YouTube
(423) cocaine manufacturing in 2023 - YouTube

Back in 2011, a deadlier form of CRACK appeared in Brazil! Name, Oxi-Oxi-dado Rust. A combination of coca paste, gasoline, kerosene, and quicklime. It's reported to be more powerful and wicked than Crack Cocaine.
(40) Brazil's Amazon in grip of deadly drug - YouTube

THE DEVIL'S BREATH*!*
(611) World's Scariest Drug (Documentary Exclusive) - YouTube

COCAINE AND PREGANCY
(1) cocaine and pregnancy - YouTube

GET HELP NEAR YOU
AT www.thegooddrugsguide.com

OPIUM PAPAVER SOMNIFERUM L. ELITE
Dangerous Beauty: A History Of the Opium Poppy - YouTube

THE FIRST AND SECOND OPIUM WARS
BETWEEN GREAT BRITAIN AND CHINA
(628) The opium wars - YouTube

THE BRITISH EAST INDIA EMPIRE
(707) the british east empire - YouTube

OPIUM IN THE 21ST CENTURY
2020 global opioid Afghanistan - YouTube
(632) 2022 global opioid Afghanistan - YouTube
https://www.youtube.com/results?search_query=Global+Opi

VISIT THE OPIUM MUSEUM
https://theopiumpipe.com/
(628) opium museum - YouTube

VINTAGE OPIUM PIPES
(628) vintage opium pipes - YouTube

OPIUM DENS
(1) opium dens - YouTube

THE HISTORY OF HEROIN
https://en.wikipedia.org/wiki/Heroin#History
www.druglibrary.org/schaffer/heroin/opiates.htm
(595) Dangerous Beauty: A History Of the Opium Poppy - YouTube

HEROIN AND RELATED IMAGES
Erowid Opiates / Opioids Vault

THE ASSASSIN FENTANYL
(40) fentanyl - YouTube

CAPTAGON
Fenethylline - Wikipedia

METHAMPHETIMINE
http://en.wikipedia.org/wiki/Methamphetamine
www.youtube.com/results?search_query=Crystal+meth

BATH SALTS, THE BOOGEYMAN
(40) Bath Salt 2022 - YouTube

PCP, THE FACTS
http://en.wikipedia.org/wiki/Phencyclidine
(1) Phencyclidine - YouTube

LSD www.youtube.com/results?search_query=LSD
IMAGES Erowid LSD (Acid) Vault

XTC
(423) ecstasy - YouTube
(639) pill xtc - YouTube

DATA AND IMAGES
AT www.ecstasydata.org

FRANCIS BURTON HARRISON
The Harrison Narcotics Act of 1914 - YouTube
www.nndb.com/people/125/000172606

THE VOLSTEAD ACT OF 1920
(629) volstead act - YouTube
(629) prohibition - YouTube

OFFICE ON DRUGS AND CRIME
www.unodc.org **STAY INFORMED**
www.ncjrs.gov

SOUTH AMERICA NEWS
www.insightcrime.org

DRUG WARS IN THE 21ST CENTURY
(632) drug wars 2019 - YouTube
(632) drug wars 2020 - YouTube
(634) drug wars 2022 - YouTube

DRUG TRAFFICKING SUB'S
(628) narco submarine - YouTube

DRUG TUNNELS
(628) narco tunnels - YouTube

MONEY LAUNDRING
(1) drug money laundering - YouTube
(628) money laundering - YouTube

BEHIND THE SCENES DRUG
TRAFFICKING AND PROSTITUTION
(634) hard drugs and prostitution - YouTube
(426) drug trafficking - YouTube
(634) Male prostitution - YouTube
(632) global prostitution - YouTube

PIMPS & ESCORT AGENCIES
http://en.wikipedia.org/wiki/Pimp
https://en.wikipedia.org/wiki/Escort_agency
http://en.wikipedia.org/wiki/Prostitution

TEEN DRUG USE
(632) teens and drugs 2022 - YouTube
(40) teens substance use internationally - YouTube

TEEN PROSTITUTION
(40) teen prostitution 2022 - YouTube

THE EXPLOITATION OF
MEN, WOMEN & CHILDREN
www.ctdatacollaborative.org/story/men-and-boys-trafficked-sexual-exploitation
Rape of males - Wikipedia
www.worldwithoutexploitation.org
(40) child exploitation - YouTube
www.childrenofthenight.org
www.missingkids.com
www.catwinternational.org
www.gems-girls.org

HUMAN TRAFFICKING, HOTLINE!
https://polarisproject.org/befree-textline

PREVENT CHILD ABDUCTION
www.childwelfare.gov/pubs/trafficking-agencies

WORLD HUMAN RIGHTS ORGANIZATIONS
http://en.wikipedia.org/wiki/List_of_human_rights_organisations

INTELLEGIENCE ON THE MOVE
www.deadiversion.usdoj.gov
www.dea.gov www.un.org
www.fbi.gov www.cia.gov

THE WORLD'S LARGEST
POLICE DEPARTMENT
www.interpol.int

NIDC www.justice.gov/archive

OFFICE OF DIVERSION CONTROL
www.deadiversion.usdoj.gov
(Code of Federal regulations)

FEDERAL DRUG CONSPIRACY CHARGES?
(634) charged with a federal drug conspiracy - YouTube

INNOCENT
www.innocenceproject.org
JUSTICE www.usdoj.gov
www.crime-prevention-intl.org

DRUG POLICY FACTS
www.drugwarfacts.org

SNITCHES, RATS
www.rats-nosnitch.com/rats/
www.snitching.org

PRIVATE PRISONS
(634) private prisons - YouTube
www.famm.org

KIDS, A REALITY CHECK!
(632) kids behind bars - YouTube
(633) teens behind bars - YouTube
(1) women in prison - YouTube

INMATE SEARCH
www.insideprison.com

DONATE BOOKS TO PRISONS
www.prisonbookprogram.org

THE MOST ASTONISHING ART
Welcome to the Justice Arts Coalition - Justice Arts Coalition

GANG AND YOUTH MENTORS
(633) gang and youth mentors - YouTube
Federal Data | youth.gov
www.mentoring.org

THE HISTORY OF PRESENT-DAY GANGSTERS
(634) the history of gangs - YouTube
(634) the history of Gangsters - YouTube
(40) the history of female Gangsters - YouTube

THE 1920's, 30's GANGSTERS
(634) Gangsters of the 1920's and 30's - YouTube

ORGANIZED CRIME IN THE AMERICAS PERSONALITIES, COUNTRIES, AND MUCH-MUCH MORE
AT http://insightcrime.org

THE AMERICAN CIVIL LIBERTIES UNION
American Civil Liberties Union (aclu.org)
www.cdc.gov

PARENT'S TALK TO YOUR KIDS ABOUT DRUGS
(703) talking to kids about drugs - YouTube

INTRODUCING THE LEGENDARY *Mel Blanc.*
TAKING YOU BACK IN TIME WITH THESE
ANTI-DRUG PSA'S FEATURING

MEL blogfiles.wfmu.org/MW/Mel_Blanc_-_Mel_Blanc.mp3
BUGS BUNNY http://blogfiles.wfmu.org/MW/Mel_Blanc_-_Bugs_Bunny.mp3
Daffy Duck blogfiles.wfmu.org/MW/Mel_Blanc_-_Daffy_Duck.mp3
YOSEMITE SAM blogfiles.wfmu.org/MW/Mel_Blanc_-_Yosemite_Sam.mp3

DRUG PREVENTION EDUCATION
www.streetdrugs.org
www.drugfreeworld.org
dare.org www.drugfree.org
www.teens.drugabuse.gov

DRUGS, POVERTY AND HUNGER
https://borgenproject.org/drugaddiction
www.childrenspartnership.org
www.wfp.org/hunger
www.worldbank.org
www.care.org

DRUGS AND THE ECOSYSTEM
(635) drugs and their contamination of the environment - YouTube

STAY IN THE KNOW!
INTERNATIONAL DRUG
POLICY CONSORTIUM
https://idpc.net

ALCOHOL ANONYMOUS
www.smartrecovery.org

WARNING!
DON'T DRINK, DO DRUGS, AND DRIVE!
(637) drugs drinking and driving - YouTube
(637) drunk driving accidents 2022 - YouTube

STAY IN THE KNOW!
365 DAYS, WITH
THESE DAILY
GOOGLE ALERTS!
DRUG PREVENTION
EDUCATION,
DRUG AWARENESS,
DRUG TRAFFICKING,
HUMAN TAFFICKING.

WHATEVER YOUR
SUBJECTS OF
INTEREST ARE!
GOOGLE IT!
www.google.com

**SUBSBUSTANCE ABUSE AND
MENTAL HEALTH SERVICES**
www.SAMHSA.gov

VETERANS HELP!
https://www.benefits.gov/benefit/307

BOOKS AT:
books.google.com
www.amazon.com
www.goodreads.com
www.draft2digital.com
www.smashwords.com
www.dymocks.com.au

**DATA, JOURNALS,
PUBLICATIONS
AND MORE.**
At www.ispub.com
www.sciencedirect.com
www.drugabuse.gov

US WORLD POPULATION
https://www.census.gov/en.html

OPEN MIC

PROSE N POETRY

CHAPTER 50

Cannabis, Hemp Facts ~

Fact #1: The use of **psychoactive** substances has occurred since ancient times and is the subject of a **well-documented** social history. There are indications that *Cannabis* was used for **medicinal** purposes as early as **4000 B.C.** in **Central Asia** and **north-western China**, with written **evidence** going back to **2700 B.C.** in the **medical book** of **Emperor Chen-Nong** containing a list of **medicinal drugs** with their effects and directions for their use.
https://thcmuseum.org/the-history

Fact #2: *Cannabis sativa* is one of the most **advanced** and extraordinary plants on the planet. It is a **monoecious, dioecious, male-female** plant that uses the sun more efficiently than any other plant on earth, reaching heights of 12-20 feet or more in a growing season of 3-6 months.

Fact #3: **Hemp** can be grown in any **climate** or **soil** condition on earth and is by far the earth's **premier renewable** natural resource.

Fact #4: **Hemp's** use for making **paper** can be traced back to China, 8000 B.C.

Fact: #5: Prior to prohibition, hemp was the PLANET'S largest agricultural crop and was the **most important industry** for producing consumer and industrial products.

Fact #6: Prior to prohibition, **hemp** produced most of the **earth's** paper, fabric, twine, carpet thread and yarn, and homespun goods, such as clothing, upholstery, towels, shoes, rope, belts, and much more.

Fact #7: Because of **hemp's** strength and its resistance to saltwater, **hemp fibers** were used to manufacture all ship canvas sails, nets, and caulking.

Fact #8: Natural hemp fibers **breathe** and are **biodegradable**.

Fact #9: **Hemp** can produce **1500** pounds of fiber per acre, whereas cotton can only produce **500** pounds per acre.

Fact #10: Over a **20-year** period, **one** acre of hemp can produce more results than **four** acres of **forestland.**

Fact #11: **Hemp** paper can be **recycled seven** times, while pulp paper can only be **recycled three** times. Hemp paper uses far less **chemical acid** than wood. In that, hemp paper is **FREE** of toxic impurities and herbicides.

Fact #12: **Hemp** paper lasts much longer than paper that is produced from **trees**. In that, it doesn't **crack, yellow,** or otherwise **deteriorate.**

Fact #13: Both the **Gutenberg** and the **King James Bibles** were printed on **hemp-based paper**. In 1776, Thomas Jefferson wrote the first two drafts of the *Declaration of Independence* on hemp paper.

Fact #14: **Hemp** can be used for **any product** that **wood pulp paper,** including the manufacturing of **diapers, newsprint, cardboard,** and **non-woven** and **absorbent goods**.
It can also be **manufactured** into **inks, paints, stains, varnishes, lubricants,** and **sealants,** as well as **industrial fabrication** materials such as **plastics, fiberboard, chipboard,** and **concrete substitute**.

Fact #15: **Hemp** grown for **biomass** makes extremely poor grade *Marijuana* for smoking.

Fact #16: **Levi Strauss (1829–1902)** was a Bavarian-American **inventor,** and the **designer** of **Levi Strauss Jeans**, made of **hemp**. In the 1960s and 1970s, these jeans experienced an **explosive** growth in the fashion industry.

Fact #17: Hemp is **four-times** warmer than cotton, is **4X'S** more **water absorbent** and has **3X'S** the **tensile** strength and is many times more **durable** and **flame retardant**.

Fact #18: During World War II, the **U.S.** government relaxed hemp laws and **urged** mid-western farmers to grow over a **million** acres of the plant for the **war** effort.

Fact #19: **Hemp seed oil** has historically been used as **lamp oil** and is **known** to be the **BRIGHTESTS** of all **lamp** oils.

Coca Facts ~

Fact #1: The **Coca** plant, and its **historic** significance dates to before the con-quest of the **Incas,** in **Andean** prehistoric times amidst small groups of **nomadic tribes** which inhabited the **Andes** during the immediate postglacial period.
· Please see
https://en.wikipedia.org/wiki/Last_Glacial_Maximum

Fact #2: The earliest **coca plants** were discovered in the Huaca Prieta settle-ment c. **2500–1800 B.C.** in the northern coast of **Peru**, positive **proof** that the **natives** of *South America* were using **coca** for a series of purposes for more than a **thousand, five hundred** years.

Fact #3: **All pre-Columbian cultures in the Andes have left evidence of usage of these leaves.** Similarly, there is ample evidence that the **coca** was the **oldest** domestic use plant in the **new** world. Its use extended over an area which includes **Perú, Bolivia, Ecuador, Colombia, Argentina, Paraguay,** and **Brazil**.

Fact #4: 1100 A.D. The **Great Inca Empire**, the citizens of **Cuzco**, to this day, hold the **Coca plant** in high esteem.

Fact #5: There are over **one hundred species** of **coca shrubs**, but the **two** most **widely used** are the **Bolivian leaf** (Erythroxylum coca) and the **Peru-vian leaf** (Erythroxylum novogranatense).

Fact #6: The **Peruvian leaf** (Erythroxylum novogranatense). Flourishes in **Colombian** and **Central American** countries.
It **differs** from the **Bolivian leaf** (Erythroxylum coca) in its **color, tex-ture,** and **odor,** and its **contents** are **lower** than the **Bolivian** (Eryth-roxylum coca).
· Please see
https://en.wikipedia.org/wiki/Erythroxylum_novogranatense
https://en.wikipedia.org/wiki/Erythroxylum_coca

These two plants have **differences** in their **appearance** and **make-up**. The **Coca Bolivia,** its **alkaloids** sets the two far apart from the remaining **98 + species** of coca shrubs.

Fact #7: During the 1880s in *Vienna*, Austria, **Sigmund Freud, Chemist** (1856–1939) studied **cocaine** as a treatment for **morphine** addiction. He also suggested the possible use of **Cocaine** as a **local anesthetic** to his **Viennese** colleagues **Leopold Konigstein**, a professor of Ophthalmology, and **Carl Koller** (1857–1944), a young Ophthalmologist.

Fact #8: **Karl Koller**, an Austrian **ophthalmologist**, first, experimented on **animals** and then presented his findings to the **Congress of Ophthalmology** in Heidelberg, Germany, in 1884. He demonstrated that **cocaine** could be successfully used as a **local anesthetic** during **eye** surgery. Koller's findings were accepted enthusiastically.

Fact #9: **Upon reaching this golden moment in history, cocaine** fulfilled all the requirements of **medication** long dreamed of by **surgeons**.

It was the **ideal anesthetic**; that could **effectively** and **reversibly block the pain impulses sent to the brain**, thus keeping the patient fully conscious without the **dangers** of chemical sleep, and more specifically, without causing "defensive behavior."

Fact #10: **In 1860**, **Albert Niemann** at the University of Gottingen was the **FIRST** to succeed in **isolating** the **cocaine alkaloid** from the **Coca leaf**. "Thanks to this **property** of the derivative it was possible to apply **2% of pure cocaine** on the nerve of a **diseased molar** and **remove** it without having a patient suffer from or be tortured by pain."

Fact #11: In the year of 1863, a **French Chemist** by the name of **Angelo Mariani** introduced a **beverage** named **'Coca Wine'** later he renamed it *Vin Mariani.* He promoted this drink as being nourishing, fortifying, refreshing and as a cure for treating a variety of illnesses, such as depression, fatigue, sleeplessness, and despondency.

Fact #12: The recipe of *Vin Mariani* **wine** was a **mixture** of **cocaine** from the **finest** of **coca leaves** and *Bordeaux* wine. His product was a **runaway**

success in North America and Europe and was consumed by a variety of celebrities and royalist who endorsed his brand.

Naming, Frederic Auguste, Bartholdi (*the Statue of Liberty sculptor*), Anatole France, Henrik Ibsen, Jules Verne, Alexandre Dumas, Massenet, Conan Doyle, and Robert Louis Stephenson. King George, the Grand Rabbi of France, Zadoc Khan, Queen Victoria of England, Pope Pius X (the tenth), and Pope Leo XIII (the thirteenth), who awarded a *Vatican Gold Medal* to the wine.

Fact #13: In 1885, **Dr. John S. Pemberton** of Atlanta Georgia, (a chemist physician and the city's druggist) created a **wine** called the **"French Wine of Coca."** a cure for **headaches, constipation, nerves, impotence, morphine addiction,** and for **relieving mental** and **physical exhaustion**. https://en.wikipedia.org/wiki/Coca_wine

Fact #14: In 1886, **Atlanta introduced PROHIBITION**.
Within the same year, **Dr. Pemberton** had to replace the **wine** in his recipe with **sugar syrup**, **coca leaf**, and **kola nut**.
At that point in time, the **French Wine of Coca** was branded **Coca Cola — The Temperance Drink**
https://en.wikipedia.org/wiki/Coca-Cola

Fact #15: **Cocaine** was used as a **recreational drug** as soon as it was **synthesized** in the 1860s. A few years after its **synthesis**, cocaine appeared in **ointments, nasal sprays,** and **tonic**.

Fact #16: **Coca** leaves were not **cultivated** only in the **Andean** region but also in several **ASAIN** countries including **Java (Indonesi**a), **Formosa (Taiwan)** and **Ceylon (Sri Lanka).**

Fact #17: **History,** the study of **Import Data** by the CADH **(Committee on the Acquirement of the Drug Habit).** Revealed a 40 percent rise in **cocaine imports** into the United States over just a four-**year** period **1898-1902**. Following the rapidly growing popularity of **cocaine use** in the **1880s** and **1890s**, North America experienced its **FIRST** cocaine epidemic at the turn of the century.

Fact #18: Recreationally! **BARS** began putting **cocaine** into **whiskey.** It was a frequently added **ingredient** to popular soft drinks.

Fact #19: **Questionnaires** were sent out to a thousand **physicians** and **pharmacists** in major towns by the **Committee on the Acquirement of the Drug Habit** suggested that the number of so-called **frequent** buyers of **cocaine** and **morphine** from **drug dealers,** increased to more than **200,000** in **1902**. Other estimates put that number at close to **400,000**.

Fact #20: Global legal **cocaine** manufactured in **1903** was 15 metric tons (two thirds of which were consumed in the USA).

Fact #21: These **cocaine** exports **declined** between 1920 and 1933. Between **1920** and **2006** global coca leaf **exports** had fallen to 47 tons.

Fact #22: **Indonesia** produce the **coca leaf** until the mid-1960s, before halting production altogether.

Fact #23: Following a massive decline of Bolivia's **LEGAL** coca leaf production between 1921 and 1933 production recovered from around 1,000 tons to expanding to 7,000 tons by **1975,** expanding to **25,200 tons** in **1980**.

Fact #24: **Adulterated cocaine is 30% Sulfate, the Fire of Hell.**

This **chemical diversity** explains the following **SERIOUS** toxic **reactions**:
· Neurological effects, strokes, seizures, and headaches.
· Gastrointestinal complications and abdominal pain.
· Nausea, blurred vision, fever, and muscle spasms.
· Thermal airway injury, coma convulsions, Chest pains.
· **Sudden cardiac death! Heart attack.**
· Irreversible or severe damage to the brain and nervous systems.
· Visceral effects on the liver, kidney, and intestines.
· Severe respiratory effects Distress and Chest pains.
· Respiratory failure, Deterioration in lung function.
· Chronic lung injury, Thermal airway injury, Coma convulsions.
· Whatcha see is Whatcha buying!

Opium Facts ~

Fact #1: The **Opium Poppy** (*Papaver Somniferum*) is an annual herb that is native to Southern Europe and Western Asia and has been an **incredibly important** plant since the Dawn of civilization.

Fact #2: **Raw opium** contains about **(twenty-five alkaloids,** all of which together constitute about **(one-fourth of the weight)** of **raw** opium. The **major** alkaloid is **morphine,** which constitutes about **(ten-to-twenty percent)** of raw opium.

Fact #3: The genus *Papaver* is the **Greek** word for **"poppy."** The species *Somniferum* means **"Sleep inducing."**

Fact #4: The **psychological** effects of **opium** were known to the **Sumerians**, the **first-known** civilization to **culture** poppy plants. At the end of the **third** millennium B.C. their name for **opium** was **"hul gil"** meaning **"the plant of joy."**

Fact #5: The **Sumerians** passed on the **benefits** of poppy to the **Assyrians**, and the Assyrians passed on the **art of poppy culling** to the **Babylonians**, who in turn passed on their knowledge to the **Egyptians**, who in turn passed on their knowledge to **archeologists**, "a person who **studies** human history and prehistory through the **excavation** of sites and other physical remains."

Fact #6: **Opium thebaicum** flourished throughout the **Mediterranean** countries as an **analgesic** and **sedative** derived from **juice** from the **seed-pod** and **leaves** of the opium poppy, which was formed into a **black pill** that was prescribed as a **painkiller**. Even the ancient **Egyptians**, **Greeks**, and **Romans** had faith in it.

Fact #7: In 1680, **Dr. Thomas Sydenham** wrote: "Among the **remedies** which have pleased the **Almighty God** to man to relieve his **sufferings**, none is so **universal** and as **efficacious** as opium."

Fact #8: Opium was known in the 18th century as the **"scared anchor of life,"** the **"milk of paradise,"** the **"hand of God,"** and the **"destroyer of grief."**

Fact #9: In the year 1836, **Friedrich Wilhelm Sertürner**, a **German pharmacist**, isolated the compound **morphine** from the opium plant. He named it after **Morpheus, the Greek god of dreams**. His discovery proved to be a **temporary** cure for **opium addiction**, which was an international concern at that time.

Fact #10: In 1853, the patented **hypodermic needle** was used to distribute **morphine** via the **blood stream** to relieve pain, and as an **intended** means to cure addiction. **Unfortunately**, the use of the **hypodermic needle** caused **morphine** to become a more **trendy way** of getting high.

Fact #11: In the year 1874, **heroin** was **first synthesized** from morphine by **C.R. Wright,** a British chemist who invented **(diacetylmorphine)**, Heroin named after the German word **(heroisch),** which means **"heroic treatment."**

Fact #12: In the year 1874, **Heinrich Dreser** conceded that **(diacetylmorphine)** Heroin was **10X'S** more potent than morphine.
He saw **Heroin** as a **commercial** opportunity for **therapeutic** uses, a **remedy** for coughing.
http://www.fohbc.org/PDF_Files/Heroin_Aspirin_Part1_CMunsey.pdf

Fact #13: In the year 1898, **Bayer AG Company** registered **heroin** and promoted it as a **non-addictive** treatment for **tuberculosis, coughs, multiple sclerosis, bronchitis, diarrhea,** and as a remedy for **morphine** addiction.

Fact #14: In the year 1902, **Bayer** launched a **worldwide** marketing campaign for **Heroin**, the results was a catastrophe.

Fact #15: In 1906, **25 million** people worldwide were **strung out** on opium.

Fact #16: In 1906, 1907, opium **cultivators** produced around **41,000** tons of opium – 5X'S the global level of **illicit** opium production in **2008**.

Fact #17: **Opium** was produced in a **huge belt**, stretching from **China** to **Indochina, Myanmar, India, Persia, Turkey,** and the **Balkan countries.** In the **21ˢᵗ century**, the production of opium is now concentrated in **Afghanistan**.

Fact #18: Despite of a **major** opium epidemic in **China** at the end of the **19th century**, there was **little** interest in suppressing a business that was so **profitable** for opium **merchants, shippers, bankers, insurance agencies** and **governments**. Many **national** economies **depended** upon opium like the **addicts** jonesing.

Fact #19: Prior to the 1909, The **Shanghai Opium Commission**, national governments and state-sponsored **monopolies** played an **active role** in peddling opium across borders. The **profits** to be made were **huge** sums of money, generating as much as **half** of the national revenues of the island states serving as **redistribution** centers. **British India** derived 14% of state income from its **opium** monopoly in 1880.

Fact #20: At the **peak** of the opium trade, tens of **millions** of Chinese citizens were **addicted** to smoking opium. A **quarter** of the **adult** male population used it **annually**. The **massive** opium imports which supplied consumers caused the country's massive foreign reserves to dwindle. China fought TWO wars against the **British Empire** to stop **opium** importation.
This brought currency outflows to a halt and created a **huge** source of **tax revenue** of which China derived **14%** of its **income** from the **opium** trade.

Fact #21: In the 1920s, opium **skyscraping** revenues ensured that there were **important** political and economic interests vested in **continuing** the opium trade.
The **League of Nations** was established as the **custodian** of the Opium Convention.

Fact #22: In 1921, smuggling **heroin** and **cocaine** into the United States was on the **increase** to such an **extent** that the customs officers were **unable** to suppress the traffic to any **appreciable** extent.

Fact #23: The **Drugs Import and Export Act** of **1922.** Drug manufacturing was **concentrated** among **European** nations, in the **United States**, and **Japan.** Guarding against **smugglers,** The U.S. Congress **control** the export of manufactured drugs under **The Narcotic Act** that required **exporters** of such drugs to possess a proper **certificate** from the **importing** country.

Fact #24: Congress **amended** the law in **1924,** prohibiting opium importation for the **manufacturing** of heroin.

Fact #25: By the mid-1940s, **hospitals** around the world was filled with **heroin** addicts.

Fact #26: In the **1960s** and **70s** heroin use **surged.**

Fact #27: In the **21st century**, synthetic OPIOIDS, is a runaway train.

OPEN MIC

PROSE N POETRY

CHAPTER 51

About the Author

Ken's interest is creative writing, research, hemp innovations, mechanical engineering, art, history, science, vintage ships, models; sports, photography, and traveling.

OPEN MIC

PROSE N POETRY

CHAPTER 52

DEAR READER

· Read the **SHOUT-OUT!** Coming up after this. It's inspiring.

· Weapons of DETERRENCE! In **Chapter 55**, you'll find a SHOWCASE of Artists' impressions you can wear, display in your home, businesses, and schools.

· **Experience "Hard Drugs, a Reality of Pain!"**

· Make **Drug Awareness** and **Drug Prevention Education** a part of your everyday life, your environment, and wardrobe.

Sincerely,
Kenneth

OPEN MIC

PROSE N POETRY

CHAPTER 53

SHOUTOUT!

To my **NEAREST** and **DEAREST** family members.

To my real friends living and real friend's gone but not forgotten.

Shoutout to the notable SOULS I've met along the way.

**SPECIAL MOMENTS IN TIME*!*
Yesterday's the past, tomorrow's
the future, but today is a gift.
That's why it's called the present.
by Bil Kean

The first poem written, was an IDEA, born.

Back in 2002. While working security at the **Century Plaza Hotel** in Los Angeles, CA. I got a call to escort the COMEDY genius **Mr. Robin Williams** to his engagement.

I've watched about every standup comedy show,
T.V. show, and movie Robin played a role in,
comical and non-comical.

Meeting the **Funny Man** in person.
That was a powerful moment.

We had 30 minutes to go heart-to-heart before
his schedule appearance that evening,
it seemed longer.

The atmosphere was relaxed. He fired the
conversation up with some humor that brought
laughter, and tears to the eyes; we talked about a couple of
his nominated films, **Good Morning Viet-Nam**, and

Dead Poet Society. For poets and writers this was
an inspiring movie.

While talking about it! I shared my plans of writing
a book of prose and poetry with a focus on
"drug prevention education."

He elevated the IDEA by sharing his experiences, and
by suggesting a couple of great designs.
The conversation was engaging.

Our time ended! What followed was comical!
I asked him for his autograph. Giving me a last
round of laughs, he scrawled it on a tiny
piece of paper; hilarious!

I found a place for it in my wallet.

Upon reaching his destination we said our last
few words and shook hands. Feeling creative
afterwards, and to add, he, and his liaison
wished me **Good Luck** with my book idea.

I took their wishes to heart.

Since my encounter with
the **Funnyman**. You know it!
I've been JAZZED up for years.

Remembering you *Robin* (R.I.P.)
(508) Experience Life - Robin Williams Motivation Tribute - YouTube
and www.youtube.com/watch?v=F4K_Dtc7VQc

In the summer of 2004, while working security
at **MTV Networks** in Santa Monica, CA.,
I was waiting for the elevator, in route to do
a patrol of the parking levels. When the doors
opened, to my surprise, there stood
Smokey Robinson.

We shook hands and embraced.

While engaged in conversation, I walked
him to his vehicle. This was another powerful
moment in time. It was great talking to *Smokey*,
whose music and poetry I've enjoyed

listening to since I was a kid going back to

Smokey Robinson & The Miracles.
The **1960s** classics, Micky's Monkey, and
My Girl, composed by *Smokey Robinson* and
Ronald White, sung by the Temptations, and
Oh yes! The Tracks Of My Tears, and The
Love I Saw In You Was Just A Mirage.
Classics Indeed!

We talked about his love for writing poetry
and my idea for authoring a book of prose and
poetry focused on "drug prevention education."

He also liked the idea*!*
After an encouraging and artistic conversation,
he blessed me with his autograph and wishes.

To Kenneth, God Bless you.
Good Luck With Your Book.
Smokey Robinson

We shook hands, embraced, wished each
other well, and parted ways.

Since my encounter with *Smokey*.
You know it! I've been
JAZZED up for years.

This **SHOUTOUT** is to you *Smokey* ~
www.youtube.com/watch?v=uYakNICSikQ

And to my mentors
Mr. Harvey Brody,
Author, Inventor,
Marketing Guru, the
King of Toll-Positions,
And Mr. Sherman W.
Hunter Sr. Business
Consultant, Software
Developer, and author
of the Concept and
(PBS) Portable Business
Strategy ©1986.

SHOUTOUT!
To The Illustrious
Richard Scott and
his inspiring wife
Irene. To Ms. Betty
Rose McKinney, and
family. To TC. Ms.
Thelma Houston and
Family. To Ms. Mary
Lucky and family.

To Mr. John Johnson,
Mr. Johnny and Zenovia
Willis, Mr. Keith Boles,
Mr. Willie Wooden,
Mr. Craton and Bobbi
Hunter, Mr. Grady

Brown, Ms. Carolyn
Lawton, and the
Lawton family,
Ms. Robi, and
Kianta.

**Entrepreneurs,
Human Dynamos.**

You know it! Since my
encounter with you all!
I've been JAZZED
up for years.

Yesterday's the past, tomorrow's
the future, but today is a gift.
That's why it's called the present.
by Bil Kean

Interior Book and Cover Design
by Nio from Poland,
one of Fiverr's best.
https://www.behance.net/Niokoba

OPEN MIC

PROSE N POETRY

· CHAPTER 54 ·

PROSE N POETRY

www.digitalpoet.net
Drug Abuse | Power Poetry
https://writers.com/prose-vs-poetry
www.familyfriendpoems.com/poems/sad/addiction

OPEN MIC

PROSE N POETRY

· CHAPTER 55 ·

WHO AM I?

A Self-Publishing, and Print On Demand Entity.

Teaching **DRUG AWARENESS** and **DRUG PREVENTION EDUCATION** that is Vital to the mind, body, and soul.

I have your wants in mind! With impeccable language and **ARTISTIC** creations, sending a **POWERFUL** message to kids, teens, young adults, and adults.

B2B, Individuals, Book Clubs, Libraries, Schools, and Colleges.

Add **"Hard Drugs, a Reality *of* Pain!"** To your reading and listening collection.

· Hardback
· Paperback
· Audiobook
· E-Book on CD, DVD, and on CUSTOM USB Flash Drive.
· Hoodies
· T-shirts
· Hats
· Drink Ware
· Posters
· Stationery
· And More.

WELCOME TO

www.drugawareness.shop

Six thousand miles away! You needn't be "out of touch."
Whatever you want, whenever you want it, we can send it to wherever in the
world you like!

Contact: Ken@drugawareness.live

OPEN MIC

PROSE N POETRY

CHAPTER 56

CLOSING

"The chances of you, someone you know,
love trying alcohol and a hard drug
ONCE are as real as the millions
counted and unaccounted for!"

To avoid a living hell
on Earth, bad health,
and life threatening pitfalls.

JAIL,
DEATH!

Don't start
drinking,
drugging,
and smoking.

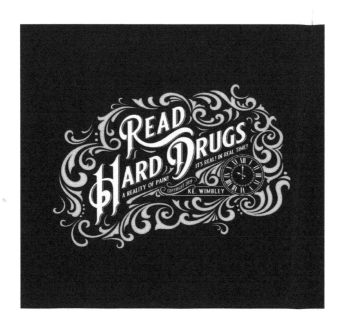

OPEN MIC

PROSE N POETRY

CHAPTER 57

AN ARTISTS IMPRESSION

KEW

DRUG AWARENESS LIVE PRODUCTIONS

‼CAUTION‼

Although many of these firms are *highly credible*. The author makes no guarantees as to the reliability of any businesses contacted through this book. **Users** of this information are solely responsible for doing their research on each business contacted. The author cannot be held liable for any damages, claims, losses, and/or expenses whatsoever resulting from the use of this information.